AMERICAN EGRET

Bird Flight

WRITTEN & DESIGNED BY

GORDON C. AYMAR

A COLLECTION OF 200
ACTION PHOTOGRAPHS

★

GARDEN CITY PUBLISHING CO., INC.
GARDEN CITY, NEW YORK

De Luxe Edition

1938
GARDEN CITY PUBLISHING CO., INC.

Copyright 1935
by GORDON C. AYMAR

TO

PEGGY, CAROL, BARBARA AND GORDON, JR.,

WHO HAVE BEEN VERY PATIENT

ACKNOWLEDGMENTS

THIS book belongs to the men whose perseverance and skill have produced the photographs of which it is composed. The hours they labored, the obstacles they overcame make it theirs. Not that anyone should feel sentimental about all this labor. It is safe to say that they loved it or they would not have done it. Perhaps it may be some satisfaction to them to see it collected in its present form. Certainly the enthusiasm and interest shown by all of them, many of whom I have never met, would lead me to hope that this may be the case.

I am particularly grateful to the members of the New York Staff of the National Association of Audubon Societies for their unfailing cooperation; to Peter Keane, Paul Hesse and C. L. Welsh for the use of cameras and lenses in taking some of my own photographs; to Warren F. Eaton who has been good enough to read the manuscript with an eye to technical errors; and to Dr. Alexander Klemin, Professor-in-Charge of the Daniel Guggenheim School of Aeronautics, New York University, who has kindly reviewed the chapter on Aerodynamics.

The photograph of Royal Terns used as end papers was taken by Stanley C. Arthur and the White Tern on the title page is shown through the courtesy of the U. S. Bureau of Biological Survey.

INTRODUCTION

THE literature on birds is voluminous. There are works treating of birds and their position in the animal kingdom, structural and functional adaptations, eggs, interbreeding, the alimentary canal and the vascular system. There is practically no phase of bird life that has not had its book. On the bird's most characteristic activity—flight—many books have been written, to be sure, but none, so far as I am aware, devoted exclusively to allowing the infallible camera to state what actually happens in the many different types of flight of the various species. That is the real justification for this book.

September 5, 1935
Noroton, Connecticut

Contents

REMINISCENT of the Pterodactyls and other flying monsters of a bygone age. The Brown Pelican has retained through hundreds of centuries the long-headed, long-winged, short-bodied form we associate with the ancient flyers.

Evolution

THE sight of a bird in flight is so familiar that it does not occur to us that this act is the culmination of a long process of development. For millions of years this process has been going on, building up in the race the perfect mastery of the air which we so easily take for granted.

To retrace the steps in this evolution with the aid of the information now available leads us inevitably to the conclusion that it is among the reptiles that we must look for the origin of the race.

Just what kind of reptiles were the forefathers of birds is a matter of conjecture. Heilmann [1] places the point of departure among the Pseudosuchians, reptiles of an extremely remote period.

Following roughly along the lines of his conclusions we can trace the slow development from the Pseudosuchians of those days to the birds of today. And if we condense the intricate work of nature through many periods and eras into a brief space we can form for ourselves a fairly clear picture of the changes that took place. First, there was the scaly, lizard-like reptile which moved on all fours. Then, perhaps through habits of feeding on objects just above its reach, this animal, so unlike a bird, raised itself more and more fre-

[1] The Origin of Birds: Gerhard Heilmann.

quently on its hind legs until they became its principal means of support.

From running along the ground it took to the trees and made its way among them by jumping from branch to branch. In order to gain a better grip the first toe changed its position and became a hind claw.

Now there occurred a change for which it is more difficult to account. As the reptile continued leaping about in the trees, the scales on the after part of its forearm, and those on the side of its tail became longer and formed small gliding planes. This modification of scales continued over the flanks and gradually extended in a lesser degree all over the body, the scales in the meantime becoming frayed at the ends and taking on more of the characteristics of feathers.

With the increased use of the arms in operating the newly acquired planes, the muscles developed and with this development came a change in the breast-bone.

From the cold-blooded, sluggish reptile this increased activity of climbing, gliding and finally flapping, changed it into a warm-blooded animal. The feathers acted as insulation to protect it from the cold.

Pseudosuchian characteristics were disappearing and traces of the bird could be seen—the arms had really become wings, the long tail had contracted and the many bones had fused into the compact mass which now holds a fan of feathers. Bones throughout the body filled with air, as the air sacs of his lungs expanded, making them an ideal framework for a flying machine.

If this bird's brain were compared with that of its ancestor it would be found to be many times the size and noticeably refined.

The Pseudosuchian has vanished. All that remains is an awkward name. From the spot on the ground where it has been crawling in the dust, a bird flies.

* * * * *

2

The Hoatzin, a bird living in the Amazon Valley, is a striking illustration of the theory that animals repeat during their own life-history, embryonic or post-embryonic, the history of their race. Hatched in trees overhanging the water, the nestlings, soon after leaving the egg, climb about the branches in the neighborhood of the nest, using not only their feet and beaks, but also their wings, which are armed with claws on thumb and fingertip. The hand is, at this period, longer than the forearm.

The growth of the primaries next the exposed thumb and finger is retarded and consequently these feathers do not interfere with the action of climbing—a stage which, as Pycraft points out, corresponds to the adults in the ancient bird fossils.

Upon the growth of the wing feathers to sufficient length so that the wing may function as a support in the air, a change comes over its structure. The claws are gradually absorbed; the arm grows at a greater rate of speed than the hand. Finally, by the end of the nesting period the flight feathers have attained almost their full growth. Here, in a few brief weeks, is reflected the laborious development of the race through hundreds of thousands of centuries.

*　　*　　*　　*　　*

It is significant that in the process of evolution from reptile to bird, so many of the species which have become extinct were flightless birds or those of relatively impaired wing-power. A particular way of life had led to the destruction of the very feature that had been developed as part of their protection.

Of some of these flightless birds we have definite knowledge. The Dodo, appropriately called *Didus Ineptus,* really a gigantic pigeon bigger than a swan, had only the rudiment of a wing. According to Herbert R. Sass, the last mention of this bird by one who saw it alive was made in the journal of the chief mate of the "Berkeley Castle" in 1681.

At an even earlier date the great flightless Rail of Mauritius vanished and the last chapter of the Solitaire of Rodriguez was written by Leguar who founded a colony there in 1691. He says of them that "they never fly, their wings are too little to support the weight of their bodies; they serve only to beat themselves, and flutter when they call to one another."

Again, the Black Emu of Kangaroo Island, South Australia, another large flightless bird, suffered extermination at the hands of man —in this case, one man, who came to the island, in the early part of the last century. At his hands an entire species was wiped out.

Before 1845 the last flightless Great Auk had disappeared, of which in 1578 Parkhurst wrote that there was one island "where wee may drive them on a planke into our ship as many as shall lade her."

Many species alive today give evidence of decreasing powers of flight. The Laysan Teal, for instance, can fly only about a hundred yards without becoming so exhausted that it is sometimes possible to capture the birds by hand.

Captain King in his narrative of the *Adventure and Beagle* says that the Steamer Duck suffers from the shortness and remarkably small size of his wings which, not having sufficient power to raise the body, are used only to propel it along like the paddles of a side-wheeler.

Darwin, who saw the Steamer Duck at the Falklands, concludes that some fly, and "others appear to be either wholly incapable of flight, or do not make use of their facilities in this respect." He expresses the opinion that it is the young birds that can fly and that the power of flight or the disposition to fly diminishes with age.

FINGERS FOR CLIMBING. Archaeornis, a reptile-like bird of the Upper Jurassic period, was about the size of a pigeon. Three fingers on each hand, each finger capped by a claw, protruded from the feathers. Painted by Gerhard Heilmann for "The Origin of Birds."

8

9

Many water birds seem to be tending towards a more specialized use of their wings in the water with diminishing powers of flexible, well controlled flight. Puffins, for example, are apparently unable to rise from the ground. Instead, they launch themselves from the edges of the cliffs where their burrows are. Grebes, also, cannot rise from the ground unless it is hard and smooth, affording them an uninterrupted runway for a take-off.

In sharp distinction to these are the species which through the long stretch of time have perfected their flying powers, the Golden Plover in endurance, the Swift in speed, the Albatross in ability to soar, the Humming-bird in control, the Duck Hawk in power of attack.

How prodigal nature has been while producing these examples of perfected flight, we can only imagine when we go over the long list of species which have become extinct within the infinitesimally short period covered by the memory of man.

II

Biology

PERHAPS the only phase of bird flight which is not highly controversial is that of anatomy. Here is a subject where facts can be determined by the examination of a large number of individual specimens under conditions satisfactory to the investigator—a situation which certainly does not hold in the study of flight itself.

Furthermore, it is a subject which, fortunately, can throw a great deal of light on the problem, for by an examination of the skeleton, organs, muscles and feathers of a bird we are collecting the basic facts on the bird as a flying machine—his skeleton being the frame; his heart, the motor; his lungs, the cooling system; his digestive system of gizzard, stomach and viscera being the treatment of fuel; his tail, the rudder and elevator; and his wings, the wings themselves.

As usual, nature has perfected a mechanism which man can never hope to duplicate. The skeleton is lightly built and, compared to its weight, gives a relatively large surface for the attachment of muscles. Another functional adaptation is the tendency of certain bones to fuse together so as to offer strong support for the strains of flying. The bones of the wing—upper arm, forearm and hand—are put together in such a way that they can be folded compactly in the shape

12

of a Z, yet they move only in one plane thus giving the wing the necessary rigidity.

The bird's organs are held within a springy framework composed of ribs, backbone and breast-bone. Around this works the girdle which corresponds to our own shoulder blades and collar bones, and which furnishes the foundation for the wings.

The degree to which the keel or center ridge of the breast-bone is developed in a bird is a good indicator of the amount of active work done by the wings. Certain species which depend largely upon soaring, such as the Albatross, have comparatively little development, while a Humming-bird's breast-bone is extraordinarily deep compared to the size of its wings. It is this keel which forms the point of origin of the large flight muscles—the "white meat" of the birds we eat.

The great flexibility of a bird's neck is of value in enabling it to see danger approaching from any direction, in catching its prey and preening its feathers. As a matter of fact, the neck of a bird has greater freedom of motion than that of a snake. In the tiny neck of a Sparrow there are 14 vertebrae; in the Swan's 23; while the neck of a Giraffe has only 7. On the other hand, the bird's backbone, except just at the waist, is particularly rigid so as to stiffen the framework against which the wings may work.

As would be appropriate for a structure built for flight, the body of a bird is not solid throughout but contains air sacs extending around viscera and muscles and in some cases filling a space between muscles and skin. Small tubes even go from lung and air sac to the bones themselves—particularly the limbs and skull. The extent to which the bones are thus aerated differs with the species—a Gannet, according to F. W. Headley, having wings, breast-bone, vertebrae, ribs and many others pneumatic, while in the Swallow even the wing bones are solid. In general, the larger birds are more completely pneumatic than the smaller ones. The fact that a Pelican, five

13

FLEXIBLE. In the tiny necks of these English Sparrows there are 14 vertebrae; in the neck of a Giraffe, 7. Taken at $\frac{1}{1000}$ of a second.

feet long, weighing 25 pounds, has a skeleton of only 23 ounces, indicates how perfectly a bird's skeleton is adapted to the function it performs.

It is worth noting that the active part of a bird's breathing is exhaling and not inhaling as in mammals. The lungs are compressed by pressure from ribs, backbone and to an extent, from the breastbone also. Certain authorities have stated that a flying bird is helped to breathe by the movements of the wings. It is difficult to see how this could be of any direct mechanical assistance unless the movement were synchronized. That this is obviously improbable is proved by comparing the rate of breathing of perching birds with the rate of wing-beat while flying. Even an extravagant allowance for the difference in the rate of breathing between perching and fly-

14

ing cannot make up for the discrepancy.

Birds, like their reptilian ancestors, do not perspire. They depend upon the air exhaled with each breath to regulate the temperature of the body, and to some extent upon the evaporation of water from the internal surfaces of the lungs and air sacs. This cooling system operates in a body whose temperature is considerably higher than that of human beings. A Swift's, for example, is 111.2° F.; a Duck's, 109.1°; a Heron's, 105.8°.[1]

A bird's breathing is rapid; his heart beats quickly; his blood has more red corpuscles per ounce than any other animal. There is a complete separation of pure and impure blood in the heart—another departure from early reptilian life—and another factor contributing to intensity and vigor of life. This high pitch to which a bird's body is tuned perhaps accounts for the richness of its song.

It takes a relatively large amount of fuel and a high rate of metabolism to keep a machine of this type working properly. Dr. Arthur A. Allen has stated that a young Robin shortly after having left its nest ate 14 feet of earthworm in one day. Young Crows are accustomed to consume at least half their own weight a day, and have been known to eat their full weight. For parental energy in supplying these needs, the House Wren holds the record. One bird was recorded as having fed its young 1,217 times during the daylight of one day.

The kind of work which a bird's muscles have to do may be judged not only from the size but, to an extent, from the color also. Those muscles which are called upon for quick but not prolonged action are paler than those capable of long continued exertion. In many game birds, such as the Partridge, Grouse and Ptarmigan, this contrast of color is particularly marked in the paleness of the elevator muscle which raises the wing, as compared with the large depressor which lowers it.

[1] The Flight of Birds: F. W. Headley.

HE DOES NOT PERSPIRE. Although the English Sparrow beats his wings 13 times a second, he does not depend on perspiration to regulate his temperature, but on the rush of air through his lungs.

The action of the elevator (*pectoralis minor*) is an interesting bit of mechanics. It is inserted into the lower surface of the breast-bone, in the angle between the keel and the breast-bone proper. It is therefore considerably below the wing which it must raise. The raising is accomplished by means of a tendon working through what would correspond to a pulley—a hole where the bones of the shoulder, (the scapula, coracoid and clavicle) join each other. The tendon passes through this hole to the upper surface of the humerus or upper arm bone. Thus, every time a bird raises its wing it is using a complete

16

block-and-tackle gear. When we consider that a Sparrow makes this motion 13 times a second, according to Hilzheimer, we get some idea of the demands made upon this part of the bird's machinery.

The strain upon the depressor or *pectoralis major,* however, is even greater. A comparison of relative sizes is sufficient to indicate the difference. The muscle which gives the downward thrust to the wing averages four times the size of the muscle which raises it. This development is due to the demand for power and speed in the down-stroke which supports the bird in the air and propels him forward. There is also this distinction: The down-stroke is made with the wing extended and offering its maximum resistance to the air, while in the up-stroke the wing is partially folded to offer less resistance. At the same time it is being lifted by pressure of the air due to the bird's momentum. The raising is, therefore, almost a passive motion except in getting under weigh.

Dr. William Beebe states that the greater pectoral muscle of a pigeon weighs one-fifth as much as the entire bird itself, bones and all. Sir J. Arthur Thomson found that in some pigeons the pectoral muscles weigh half the whole bird. This checks exactly if we take the lesser pectoral muscle as weighing one quarter that of the greater.

It has been calculated that the energy expended by a pigeon when taking flight is five times as great as when it has acquired its average speed. It is at this time, therefore, that the greater pectoral muscle must do its heaviest work. In order to insure the maximum velocity for the outer expanse of the wing, the muscle is attached to the upper arm bone close to the shoulder. A small motion at this point means a large motion at the wing tip. But this type of leverage is far from being economical of energy—hence the great development of the depressor.

A bird is kept from falling off his perch when asleep by an ingenius device. When he sits down his knees and ankles bend and this bending automatically tightens the tendon running along the bony lower leg. This tendon contracts the toes which grip the perch and thus prevent the bird from falling.

If a bird is to travel through the air at speeds varying from 20 to 70 miles an hour, and if he is to be able to see his prey on the ground or in the air, his vision must be not only extraordinarily acute, but capable of quick changes in focus as well. In this function of accommodation of the eye, birds excel all other animals. In other vertebrates focusing is accomplished through muscles acting upon the lens. In a bird's eye there is, in addition, a provision by which the curvature of the cornea is altered also, giving a two-fold control.

In addition to this ability of focusing quickly, a bird is endowed with unusually keen eyesight. A Vulture soaring hundreds of feet in the air can detect movements on the ground which it would be quite impossible for the human eye to see. Anyone who has hunted either with gun or camera can testify to this sharpness of vision in birds. The Hawk on the falconer's wrist cocks his head to watch a bird high in the air long before the bird is discovered with binoculars.

The physiological basis for this superiority appears to rest in the foveae which are small areas of most acute vision. A man's eye has one such area; many species of birds have two and in the Swift, the Swallow, and the Tern there are three. It is significant that the fastest and most accomplished flight and the most complex formation of the eye are found together.

Another point in which the bird's eye differs from that of a man is its lack of mobility. This would be a serious handicap, either in hunting or in being hunted, if there were not compensation for it in the remarkable mobility of the bird's neck.

Further protection is given by the placing of the eyes on the sides of the head, with a consequent increase in the field of vision. The extremes in the matter of position are found in a bird that is hunted and one that hunts. The Woodcock feeds at night in damp spots, probing for its food in the mud. In this vulnerable position it has need, literally, of eyes in the back of its head to protect it from the attacks of predatory creatures. And that is almost where the eyes are placed—well back from the normal position and quite far up toward the top of the head. On the other hand, the Barn Owl, the hunter, looks straight ahead in the manner of men and monkeys. Flying at night at no great height, he must concentrate on the ground for his prey.

There is a common misconception about the eyesight of an Owl, the general idea being that the bird is "blind" during the daytime. As a matter of fact, due to the power of controlling the contraction and expansion of the iris, most Owls can see in the daylight, and yet have the additional advantage of keen sight during the dim light at night.

A bird's eye is endowed with a third eyelid, called the nictitating membrane, the vestige of which we still have in our own eye in the inner corner. This membrane serves to keep the eye moistened and free from dust and in the case of such birds as Owls, to soften the strong light of day. Even with this membrane over the eye a bird can distinguish much that is going on. The Eagle, which is popularly supposed to be unique in its ability to look directly at the sun, does so by protecting its eyes with this membrane.

There is one point in which the eye of a bird appears to be inferior to that of a man, and that is in the range of its sensitivity to color. According to Sir J. Arthur Thomson [2] a bird's vision and man's are practically the same toward the orange-yellow end of the spectrum, but the bird's falls far short on the blue-violet end. In fact, he states that birds cannot see blues and violets. How far further investigation will support this belief remains to be seen. It would certainly seem to be desirable for a bird to be able to distinguish these colors if only from the point of view that the brilliant blues and violets in the plumage of certain species appear to have been developed as a matter of sex attraction.

[2] The Biology of Birds: J. Arthur Thomson.

TRIPLY KEEN. A man's eye has but one fovea, or point of extremely acute vision. This Cabot Tern, about to alight, has three.

Perhaps the most interesting part of the biology of a bird lies in that feature which distinguishes it from all other animals—namely, feathers. Here is a specific development which has come into existence to satisfy a specific need. If we trace their origin we find that they have evolved from skin structures whose early stages have much in common with corresponding stages of growth in the scales of both fish and reptiles. Oddly enough, there also exists through this same channel a kinship between a bird's feathers and an animal's teeth.

Dr. Beebe describes the complicated development of a feather

20

clearly and concisely.[3] "In the young bird slender fingers of cells grow out and split longitudinally into a number of folds which gradually dry apart and harden into the slender, silky filaments which we know collectively as down. At the base of, and in fact attached to, the down is a second set of cells which will push the down feather out of its socket. This is the true feather from which the down is rubbed or brushed off. These feathers are, when they first appear above the skin, rolled tightly in horny sheaths. In many young birds, the feathers remain in this condition until they are nearly full-grown.

The highest forms of birds, such as Crows or Thrushes, are hatched almost naked; while birds lower in scale—as our Quail—are born covered thickly with down and with wings nearly feathered, and in a few days can fly and find their own food. . . .

Each feather is composite—feathers within feathers. The quill gives off two rows of what are called barbs which together form the vane of the feather; each of these barbs has two rows of barbules, and these give rise to a series of curved hooks, known as barbicels, which work into opposite series of grooves so tightly that air cannot force its way through the feather."

The almost inconceivable intricacy of this arrangement can be appreciated when we consider that it has been estimated that there are on one primary feather of a pigeon some 1,200 barbs; that one barb on the *narrow* part of the vane has roughly 550 barbules. Regarding this as two-thirds the size of the average barb, there are approximately 990,000 barbules on *one* feather. Complicate this further by taking into account the number of barbicels on a feather and the number of feathers on a bird and the figures become almost astronomical.

That a living organism should attain its greatest usefulness after it is dead is somewhat surprising, yet it is true in the case of a feather. Upon attaining its full growth the opening at the base of

[3] The Bird: William Beebe.

the quill closes, the blood can no longer enter and it becomes lifeless. Nevertheless, as often as a feather is removed from a living bird, another will grow in its place.

It is only natural that the hard usage to which the wing and tail feathers are subjected should show its effect. Worn, broken and ragged feathers would affect the bird's powers of flight. Nature provides for replacing these by the process of molting. Some species molt once a year, others as many as two or three times. Some have a spring molt which provides them with breeding plumage, while others depend on a fall molt to equip them for a strenuous migration.

The system by which land birds shed their primary wing feathers is further testimony of the infinite care with which nature protects the survivors of her races. In order not to interfere with the bird's power of flight, the primaries are shed a pair at a time, one from the right wing and one from a corresponding position on the left wing. Not until the new pair of feathers is almost fully grown does the second pair fall out.

Certain water birds—among them Ducks and Geese—molt all the primaries at once and become incapable of flight. In order to protect themselves they fly, just before the molting period, to bodies of water where they may at least be removed from land enemies.

This method of seeking protection would serve reasonably well if it were not for the persistence and ingenuity of man's attack. In the island of Kolguev, the inhabitants drive thousands of molting geese, which have lost the power of flight, into great nets to provide themselves with food for the long Arctic winter.

Auks, Guillemots and Puffins, all of which are good divers, molt their primaries all at once, as do most of the Rails.

Dr. Robert Cushman Murphy found that the Diving Petrels off the coast of Peru were "not highly dependent upon the power of flight, because they molt their wing quills all together and thus for a time each year become exclusively aquatic. The stomachs of such crippled, Penguin-like birds, however, are as well filled with crustaceans or little fishes as those of their flying brothers." [4]

In certain birds such as the male Mallard there is an "eclipse" plumage which occurs during this extensive molt and which renders the bird less conspicuous by giving him the dusky plumage of the female.

There is still another way in which some birds change the color of their plumage—that is by the breaking off or fraying of the edges of each feather. Snowflakes, for example, change from rusty to black and white, and the male English Sparrow takes on a clear black throat.

There is one peculiarity in the structure of a feather with which many people are not familiar. If we take any blue feather and pound it the color will change to black. The reason for this lies in its pigmentation. Blue feathers contain a brown or yellowish pigment encased in a horny coating and beneath this coating is a layer of cones which act as prisms and transmute the color of pigment and sheath to blue. With one known exception, the same is equally true of green feathers. The beautiful iridescent green of the Hummingbird becomes a lifeless gray under the microscope. The blacks, reds, browns and yellows in feathers are almost always due solely to the pigment in the vane.

Undoubtedly, that part of the bird which has received more attention than any other is the wing. It has always symbolized flight and on it, from Icarus to the most recent experimenter, man has based his study of how to fly. Leonardo da Vinci constructed a wing to be worked by a series of pulleys in direct imitation of the skeleton of a bird. The almost endless series of efforts to imitate flapping flight have all proved failures, and not until the wind screw was artificially grafted on the wing held rigidly in soaring position was

[4] Bird Islands of Peru: Robert Cushman Murphy.

any degree of success in man's flying attained.

For the bird, the soaring position is merely one of an incalculable number. He must not only support himself in the air, but propel himself forward and also use his wings as brakes. He adds the final touch of complication by parking them compactly at his sides, a convenience which man has not been bold enough to imitate universally as yet.

To serve these complex demands, the bird has separate series of feathers attached to the separate bones of arm and hand. The feathers most active in propelling—the feathers of the outer wing—are attached to the bones of the hand. These are the primaries. They are closely packed along what amounts to a single bone, for the hand has become reduced to the first and second fingers which are welded together, and to the small stump of a thumb from which springs the little bastard wing or alula.

The lower arm consists of ulna and radius, as does our own, and to the ulna are attached the secondaries—the flight feathers of the inner wing. These are the feathers which play so large a part in supporting the bird in the air, moving as they do through a smaller arc than the primaries. The separate and distinct use of these two series of feathers can be readily seen in a particular type of flapping flight used at times by pigeons. During this flight the inner half of the wing appears almost stationary while the outer half is quickly flexed in short power drives.

The feathers arising from the upper arm bone or humerus are known as the tertiaries or tertials. In effect they form a further extension of the secondaries to close the gap between the active wing and the body. In most birds these feathers are few in number but in those species in which the upper arm bone is long, such as Gulls, Herons or Albatrosses, they are quite fully developed.

The flight feathers of the wing are so arranged that each feather is overlapped by the one next it nearer the base of the wing. In this

STRANGE ADAPTATION. The lower mandible of the bill of the Black Skimmer is at least a fifth longer than the upper mandible. Both are thin and pliable. It obtains its food by flying close to the surface of the water, dipping its lower mandible below the surface and scooping up whatever small crustaceans or fish may be there.

way the air pressure on the under side of the wing caused by the down-stroke, or even in gliding or soaring, forces the feathers into an air-tight fan. On the up-stroke the feathers part and air is allowed to pass between them, thus reducing unfavorable pressure.

Among certain birds that have the power of soaring, such as Vultures, Ravens, Eagles and certain Hawks, there is one very noticeable peculiarity. The outer primaries in both flapping and soaring flight separate at the tips giving almost the appearance of outstretched fingers. These gaps are formed by a narrowing of the

25

outer portion of the vane of the feathers. The aerodynamic significance of this will be discussed later. It is interesting to note here, however, that in order to prevent these "notched" feathers from separating too widely there is a rough friction surface on the overlapped portion of the feather which integrates with the surface of the feather above it to insure a tight bond. This friction surface is ingeniously and economically formed by separate hooks extended above the regular barbicels.

The perfect adaptation of a feather to its function is easy to demonstrate. Examine one of the primaries of a pigeon, for example. It can be bent double on its shaft—elasticity sufficient to withstand the average blows to which it may be subjected and to flex with air pressure to avoid creating unfavorable eddies. Its lightness is proverbial. Its shaft is curved to fit into the pattern of the whole wing with a subtlety only possible in something which nature has grown. If it is held between the fingers and swung through the air edgewise its resistance is inconsiderable; if it is rotated so that its flat vane faces the direction of motion its parachute-like character seems out of all proportion to its size. The forward or cutting side of its web is narrow like a well trimmed jib; the side aft of the shaft is broad and might well serve as a pattern for a Marconi mainsail. Its barbs are the ideal battens to keep the sail at perfect fit. Separate the barbs on any part of the web except at the base where they become downy, and they part reluctantly; smooth them together with a single stroke and they adhere again as though they had never been parted. They are the perfect instruments to extract the maximum resistance from a medium as thin as air.

In a like manner each part of a bird-skeleton, muscles, heart, lungs, digestive system—points to a development in which flight is the major consideration. This is the result of a pains-taking process of evolution—a stretch of years which, viewed in perspective, makes our achievement of flight seem almost instantaneous.

26

EXTRA LONG. In certain species, such as Gulls, Herons and Albatrosses, the upper arm bone is unusually long. From it spring the tertiaries. The photograph shows a Herring Gull about to alight.

27

DESIGN FOR SOARING. There are records of a Wandering Albatross, which measured 11 feet 4 inches from wing tip to wing tip. This great length comes from the elongation of the arm bones. In other words, the hand, from which spring the primary feathers, remains of average proportion while

28

the other bones increase relatively, with the result that there are as many as 40 secondary feathers growing from the forearm. A Humming-bird's wing has 10 primaries, an Albatross's the same number; but a Humming-bird has only 6 secondaries to the Albatross's 40.

The Albatross is one of the most completely "pneumatic" of all birds—every bone is filled with air-sacs except the scapula and hyoid. The bones being hollow are light, yet large enough to give a good surface for the attachment of muscles.

Due to the fact that the Albatross soars a great deal and flaps little, its breast-bone is shallow and the wing muscles are relatively small. A Humming-bird, on the other hand has an enormous breast-bone to provide for the machinery of its quickly-beating wings.

Notice how narrow the Albatross's wings are. An adult with a spread of 11 feet will have a wing only 9 inches wide. Besides being able to attain high speeds on practically motionless wings, the Albatross covers great distances. There is a record of a bird captured off the coast of Chile which had a small vial around its neck containing a note saying that it had been released from a whaling vessel 800 miles off the coast of New Zealand. The difference in date of release and recapture was eight days—the distance in a straight line 3,400 miles. The bird shown in the photograph is a Spectacled Albatross.

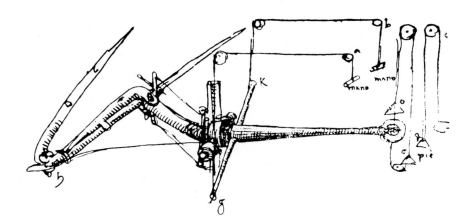

IMITATION. From time immemorial man has tried to imitate a bird's flight by mechanical means. This sketch shows a design by Leonardo da Vinci.

MASTER OF TWO ELEMENTS. The Gannet is an example of a bird which has developed marked ability in the water without correspondingly reducing its powers of flight. It lives on fish which it catches by spectacular dives of 60 to 100 feet in height. After the dive, if it is not immediately successful, it pursues the fish under water. W. B. Alexander, in "Birds of the Ocean," says that Gannets have been caught in fishermen's nets at a depth of 90 feet.

Their usual flight is direct, steady and rather close to the water, although when they are in the vicinity of a school of fish, they will cruise at diving height.

Nature has provided them with special adaptations to fit them for their particular way of life. Their toes are all enclosed within one web. In the adult birds the nostrils are entirely closed. The tongue has become relatively unimportant. Many of the bones are filled with air, and there are large air cushions beneath the skin that covers the breast—a protection which must ease the shock of their powerful dives.

The photograph shows clearly on the left wing the large membrane which stretches straight from the body to the wrist. It is particularly broad in the Gannet and, when extended, makes the wing deeply concave toward the body.

30

MASTER OF ONE ELEMENT. Study the wings of these King Penguins. They represent an episode in the course of evolution. In their first stage they were the fins of their ancestors the fishes; then the fore-paws of their ancestors the reptiles; next the wings of their ancestors the flying birds; now, having reacted through the long effect of environment, they have lost the power of flight, and have become, outwardly at least, fins again. They will never become true fins, however, for one law of nature is that she never repeats. The body of the Penguin is covered with small, scale-like feathers, having small vanes and broad shafts. The wing is like that of a shark's fin, flat and broad. Wrist and elbow have lost their flexibility. Dr. Beebe says that in the three flightless groups of birds are found the extremes in number of primaries, Penguins having approximately 36, Ostriches 16, and Cassowaries perhaps 2 feathers which can be called primaries.

The construction of the tail of the Black Footed Penguin illustrates to what extent adaptation to the water has taken place. The bones have become elongated and the flesh around them is formed into a kind of vertical rudder controlled by strong muscles. This rudder is of material assistance to the flippers.

31

APPRENTICE. Clumsy in build, clumsy in performance, the Tufted Puffin gives the impression of being a novice at flying. It rises from the water with difficulty except in a breeze and prefers to launch itself recklessly from a cliff rather than rise directly from the ground. Its relatively small wings, however, beat with great rapidity and give it considerable speed in the air. The tail is apparently subordinated to the feet in steering both in the air and under water. Those who have watched them "flying" below the surface of the water say that the wings are extended but the primary feathers are kept parallel to the body.

32

RUDDERLESS. To all intents and purposes the tail feathers of the California Murre are so short as to be of little use in steering. Instead, the webbed feet are used to help, probably as much for maintaining balance as for the effect on the air stream. These birds, like the Puffins, have become so largely aquatic that their power of flight is impaired. They fly rapidly but with no buoyancy. The Great Auk, closely related, completely lost the ability to fly and has become extinct. When startled the Murre attempts to escape by diving rather than flying. Perhaps in a million years or so Penguin-like characteristics may appear.

33

BIG. When Dr. Robert Cushman Murphy of the American Museum of National History was in Peru, one of his companions shot an old male Condor
which weighed 26½ pounds and measured just over 10 feet between extended
wing tips. This makes the Condor the second largest bird having the power
of flight, the largest being the Wandering Albatross with a spread of 11 feet
4 inches.

William Finley, who has made a life study of birds and bird photography,
in referring to the rare California species shown here, says that the growth of
these enormous birds is slow. From the time the single egg is laid, it takes six
months or even longer for the parents to raise their young.

There is a popular misconception to the effect that the Condor often carries
its prey. That this cannot be the case is proved by a study of its claws which are
blunt and weak, in no way resembling those of the average bird of prey.

34

35

SMALLEST. "The Humbird is one one of the wonders of the Countrey, being no bigger than a Hornet, yet hath all the demensions of a Bird, as bill, and wings, with quills, spider-like legges, small clawes: For colour she is as glorious as the Raine-bow; as she flies, she makes a little humming noise like a Humble-bee: wherefore shee is called the Humbird." So wrote William Wood in 1634. With a length ranging from 3 to less than 4 inches, a nest 1½ inches in outside diameter, and eggs ½ inch long, the Ruby-throated Humming-bird is the smallest bird in the East.

By the structure of their bones, such as they are, they are more nearly related to the Swifts than to any other family. Their entire wing spread is from 4 to 4¾ inches, yet these wings can drive them at least a mile a minute. To do this the breast muscles have become developed to a greater degree, probably, than those of any other bird.

They are apparently fearless, as they will even attack Hawks, Crows, or Eagles.

The Ruby-throat makes non-stop flights during migration of at least 600 miles to Bermuda and 500 miles across the Gulf of Mexico to Yucatan.

36

MARGARET L. BODINE

37

ACT OF FAITH. To launch into the air with the shabby equipment of this immature California Brown Pelican smacks of a miracle. The outer primaries are forced forward into the extreme "anti-stalling" position. The bird on the ground is about to take off. It is one of the paradoxes of flight that a bird of such clumsy build, five feet long, can support himself in a medium such as air.

PNEUMATIC. A Brown Pelican landing. A Pelican's bones are so thoroughly aerated that a bird weighing 25 pounds has a skeleton of only 23 ounces. The perfect poise of this bird indicates what extraordinary muscular coordination takes place in every movement of a bird's body. The portion of the ear devoted to maintaining equilibrium is highly developed in most birds.

SILENT. The Barn Owl's flight is buoyant and, above all, soundless. While the Pheasant rises with a loud whir of stiff quills, the Owl slips over the fields and among the trees without any perceptible noise. This is due to the formation of the flight feathers which are of great breadth and are covered with a soft pile.

One of the most noticeable features of the Barn Owl is the set of its eyes. Most birds' eyes are set on the side of the head; the Owl's face forward like those of a human being. For the Barn Owl is a hunter and flies not far above the ground, generally in a dim light, so that eyes set in this way would be particularly effective. The Woodcock, on the other hand, a bird that is hunted, and one whose bill is often buried deep in the mud, carries his eyes far back and well toward the top of his head.

An Owl can see perfectly well in the day time, by means of an automatic adjustment of the iris. In common with other birds, the Owl has a "third eyelid" or membrane which it can draw over its eye to dim the sharp light of the sun.

40

[Left] A FEATHER MAGNIFIED 18 TIMES. The column at the left is the shaft showing part of the web cut away. The parallel lines in the web are barbs. The fringe growing from the barb is made up of barbules. It has been estimated by competent authorities that there are not less than 990,000 barbules on *one* primary feather of a pigeon. The micro-photographs shown above were made in England by Arthur E. Smith especially for this book.

[Right] MAGNIFIED 100 TIMES. The dark column-like shapes are barbs. The diagonal lines are barbules. The small dots on the barbules are barbicels or hooks which hold the barbules of the neighboring barb. Notice that the barbules on the right side of each barb appear straighter than those on the left and seem to have spiral convolutions to receive the hook-like barbicels.

41

ALFRED J. MEYER

42

ACCURATE. To fly through a three inch crack would seem to be a difficult undertaking, but these Barn Swallows accomplish it with almost undiminished speed. This means not only perfect muscular control, but an exceptional ability in changing the focus of vision. In this respect birds are superior to all other animals. In addition to having a set of muscles which act directly upon the lens of the eye, they are able to alter the curvature of the cornea also.

PHOSPHORESCENT? Legend has it that the Black-crowned Night Heron throws out a light from its breast to attract fish at night. Reputable eye witnesses claim to have seen the light, even to have shot one while the light was shining, but so far no qualified ornithologist has confirmed these observations.

IGNOBLE. Feeding on carrion, offal and filth, the Black Vulture is doomed to go through life bearing the name of *Coragyps atratus atratus*. Its claws, like the Condor's, are weak compared with those of the genuine birds of prey, and it does not attack living animals. Wings and tail are shorter than those of the Turkey Vulture and its flight is more labored. The great breadth of its wing near the body combined with the shortness of tail gives the appearance when soaring of one almost continuous surface. When gorged and startled Vultures will often regurgitate their food to lighten themselves for flight.

NOBLE. From time immemorial the Osprey has been classed by falconers among the noble hawks—hawks which descend upon their prey in a splendid dive or "stoop," rather than those which chase and overtake their prey. The claws are long and powerful, the toes armed with hard spine-like scales. The wings of the bird in the photograph are forming a parachute to check speed as he returns with nesting material which is constantly replenished. Notice that the long legs, which are almost in attacking position, seem to come from the very center of the bird, putting the entire weight directly behind the strike.

45

DECEIVED. This Osprey, or Fish Hawk, is just rising from a precipitous dive. His prey, however, turned out to be a foot-long decoy of wood with celluloid fins, anchored six inches below the surface of the water. He "bound to" the fish, rose with fish and anchor, only to have the decoy slip from his talons. The splash just below him was made by the decoy.

The Osprey is the only Hawk which can reverse its outer toe so as to form the two and two arrangement common to Owls. All other Hawks and Eagles have the usual three and one form.

Notice the length of the leg when extended in striking position and the curve of the talons. Harold McNulty tells me that while fishing off Sandy Hook, he saw an Osprey dive and, after a struggle, disappear beneath the water. No trace was found of it until two days later when the body, with talons locked in the back of a four pound weakfish, was washed ashore.

46

BILL-FISHER. The Kingfisher, unlike the Osprey, catches fish with bill instead of claws. Its feet are small and weak; its bill long, large and sharp. Half closing capable wings, it shoots head first into the water. In common with certain hawks it is able to hover over the spot of attack. The exertion required for this type of flight must be many times that of ordinary flying. I have followed the rhythm of a Kingfisher hovering in almost motionless air and estimated that its wings beat at least 8 times a second. This photograph is an extremely skillful shot of an adult female leaving the nest. Mr. Howard Cleaves has made a clean hit—the bird in perfect focus, the hole, his "point of departure," being just out of focus. The wings are halfway through the upstroke—the inner half having completed it, the outer half just starting up. The primaries of one wing have opened up to allow the air to pass through with the least resistance. The angle, too, is a favorable one for the stroke.

47

HERALDIC. Audubon's Caracara has been characterized as neither Hawk, nor Vulture, nor Eagle, yet in the guise of the last named it appears on the coat-of-arms of Mexico. Its wing action is rapid compared with its progress through the air. The widely separated primaries shown below identify the Caracara with the soaring Hawks. It has unusually long legs and tail.

GREGARIOUS. Cabot and Royal Terns have the happy faculty of nesting in colonies together—apparently without getting their families mixed. The Cabot is slightly larger and relatively more slender than the Common Tern. The Royal is one of the largest of the family, with a length up to 21 inches and a spread up to 44 inches. The Cabot's tail is slightly forked; the Royal's deeply.

49

ARTHUR A. ALLEN

GULL IN A GALE. A Bonaparte's Gull in winter plumage taken during a forty mile blow. This small Gull, averaging only a little over 13 inches in length, had no difficulty whatever even during the worst gusts. The shot was made almost straight down from the deck of a lighthouse tender, yet the tail has rotated so far to maintain balance that the under side is entirely visible.

GULL IN A TREE? Not quite so incongruous as might be supposed, for this is a Bonaparte's Gull in breeding plumage, and unlike the rest of the Gull family which nest on cliffs or on the ground, this species nests in coniferous trees, even 15 or 20 feet from the ground. It is wearing its full nuptial plumage.

INADEQUATE RUDDER. The Mallard, as is the case with the rest of the Duck family, is not equipped for making quick changes of course. The tail is short, small in area and weak. An interesting comparison has been made of the Sparrow Hawk, whose tail is long and broad, and which has a very flexible flight and the Duck, which has a short tail and inflexible flight. The tail of the Sparrow Hawk measured around 8 inches; the Duck's, 4¾ inches. The Hawk weighed 5.3 ozs.; the Duck, 1 lb. 15.7 ozs. In other words the length of tail for each pound weight of the birds would be 24.1 inches for the Hawk against only 2.3 inches for the Duck—proportionately almost 11 times the length. This photograph was taken at $\frac{1}{825}$ of a second, as the bird landed.

52

53

ROBERT CUSHMAN MURPHY

PIRATE. The Skua has been called the most predatory of all sea birds. Fish, flesh, good red herring, eggs, weaker birds and their food—all are included in the Skua's diet. The tail is characteristically broad, short and slightly upturned. The Skua is stocky of build with wings designed for both speed and power. The photograph taken at South Georgia Island by Dr. Murphy shows the great breadth of the primary feathers. The Skua's flight, in its suggestion of reserve power, resembles that of an Eagle rather than a Gull. Unlike the Eagle, however, the bones of the Skua are only partially aerated.

NEW FEATHERS. In common with other Gulls, the Ring-bill passes through a series of molts—partial in spring, whole in autumn—until the bird is two years old. A. C. Bent says that some birds retain traces of immature plumage even during the third year. The Gull at the top is in full mature plumage—white spot on primaries, full white tail. The Gull at the bottom is in the final second year plumage—white tail with sharply defined dark band. The one above him is in a less advanced stage—tail not so white, band less defined, more dark on the primaries. The Duck below is a Lesser Scaup.

54

55

ALARMED. Two photographs of a Crow taken by two cameras a fraction of a second apart. The bird jumped back and up. The first picture shows the beginning of the upstroke—wrist elevated and primaries being pulled directly after it. The tips of the primaries indicate that they are still pressing down— interesting evidence of one motion blending into another. Even the tail is used in pushing. Number two is apparently the finish of this same up-stroke. Here again two actions are taking place at the same time. The uppermost primaries in the Crow's right wing are still moving up while the others have begun to move down. Great flexibility of shoulder is characteristic of these birds. Their rate of metabolism is high—a young Crow being able to consume its own weight of food each day and requiring half of that amount merely to survive.

VERDI BURTCH

C. F. STONE

MUSCULAR. A Pigeon's pectoral muscles, which raise and lower the wings, weigh as much as 50% of the entire bird. Those of the Herring Gull, a bird which flaps slowly and glides, weigh 16%. The extraordinary development of these muscles in the Pigeon enables it to rise almost vertically and to fly with a speed which is known to exceed 60 miles an hour. F. W. Headley weighed the wings of a Pigeon cut off close to the body and found that they were only ⅓ of an ounce each. The wing balanced at a point ⅕ of the length of the wing from the base, showing the extent to which feathers alone constitute the real length of the wing. The King Pigeons in the photograph are rising. Every tail is spread to give the greatest possible support and to receive the air displaced by the wings. Notice the balancing function of the tail on the bird second from the left. This Pigeon is just going into the fastest part of the up-stroke.

57

CONTROL. If it is true that straws tell which way the wind blows, this Osprey is heading into it upon landing on the nest. Perfect balance is indicated in the set of wings and tail. Notice how wide and symmetrically the tail is spread to offer its greatest resistance to the wind in order to check speed.

ATTACK. A Red-shouldered Hawk striking an Owl. The Owl, in this case, was a dummy, which accounts for its indifferent attitude. Notice the great length of the Hawk's legs when fully extended. Also the breadth and roundness of wing. This is the wing of a typical soaring hawk—a bird which hunts from a great height, and attacks from above. Cooper's and Sharp-shinned Hawks, on the other hand, perch until the prey is within range, and then give chase. Their wings are short and rounded for bursts of speed. The light area on the wing, giving the effect of translucence, can be seen in this picture.

HOWARD H. CLEAVES

WING-STEERING. The outer half of one wing of this Red-headed Woodpecker is advanced with feathers separated; the outer half of the other wing is retarded. The Woodpecker's wing is broad, rounded—somewhat suggestive of that of his fossil ancestor, *Archaeornis*. There is another similarity—a short first primary. This can be seen in the photograph just beyond the little bastard wing. In the ancient bird this shortening of the primaries near the thumb was to avoid interfering with the claws of the hand which were used in climbing. Is it possible that the resemblance in the two climbers is more than superficial?

EIGHT FOOT SPREAD. The female of the Bald Eagle may have a wing spread up to eight feet, and may weigh as much as twelve pounds.

The Eagle has always been noted for his ability to look directly at the sun. This he does, however, by drawing a membrane or extra eyelid over his eyes to protect them. His sharpness of vision is undoubtedly great. Dr. E. H. Eaton watched an Eagle soaring high overhead, dive diagonally after a dead fish floating on the surface of a lake three miles from the spot over which the bird had been soaring.

The young eaglet takes daily flying exercises which consist of flapping and hopping, during which he may rise several feet above the nest—even soaring over the edge of the eyrie, but always with feet down, ready to land.

Dr. Francis H. Herrick, says that these Eagles have a history of more than 80 years in the neighborhood in which this picture was taken. This same nest had been occupied without a break for 35 years by the same pair or their successors. The nest, added to each year, was 12 feet high and 8½ feet wide. It finally fell, killing the young, and its weight was estimated at two tons.

62

WORRIED. This Avocet is concerned over the fact that one of its young is being held in the hand of the boy. A favorite trick of many birds, when intruders are in the vicinity of the nest, is to hobble about dragging one wing as though wounded, in the hope of diverting the enemy from the young. There are few more picturesque birds than the Avocet with its long legs, long, slender neck, and elongated bill curved *up* at the tip. The peculiarly shaped bill is used to secure insects, mollusks and small aquatic life in soft mud. In normal flight, the legs are stretched stiffly out behind in the manner of a Heron, to counterbalance the neck, and the ample wings support the body with apparent ease.

64

LIGHT "LOADING." A wing-spread up to 6 feet to support a body which may weigh under 3 pounds. That is the aerial economy of the Osprey. One important feature of flapping flight is clearly demonstrated in this photograph. The wings have rotated so far that the rear margins (bounded by the tips of the flight feathers) are at the moment nearer each other than the forward margins. This rotation is necessary on the down-stroke to insure a component which will thrust air backward as well as downward. I have watched an Osprey climb steeply over a wooded hill. His wing area was so large that at every stroke his body not only rose and fell, but rocked backward and forward.

65

© BROWN BROTHERS

ONE IN A MILLION. The kind of picture a photographer dreams of getting. There have been many fanciful tales of the burdens which Eagles carry. Authorities vary in their estimates, which range from 8 to 10 or 12 pounds. One Bald Eagle has been reported as having carried a lamb over a distance of five miles. It is not surprising that a mechanism capable of carrying such extra loads, should be able, when unloaded, to soar with ease.

There seems to be one authenticated case, at least, of a Golden Eagle attacking a child. Edward H. Forbush investigated this and found that a girl of nine had been attacked and her arm much discolored and cut before her father was able to dislodge the bird and the mother to kill it with an ax. The Golden Eagle, closely related to the bird in the photograph, hunts in the grand manner. Soaring at great heights, he half closes his wings, shoots down upon his prey at full speed, and disables or kills it at a blow. This is somewhat different from the Bald Eagle, which usually lives on fish, carrion, or whatever booty it can take from the Osprey.

Incidentally, artists often represent the national bird inaccurately—making the feathered trousers extend all the way down to the feet, which is correct for the Golden Eagle but not the Bald or American Eagle.

MARAUDER. A photographic "scoop" by Alfred M. Bailey of the actual attack of a Man-o'-war-bird on a Booby. The Booby has dropped the fish and the attacker is swooping down to catch it while it is still in the air. The Man-o'-war or Frigate Bird, as it is sometimes called, with its long, hooked bill, will often attack its prey with force enough to dislocate a wing.

68

AERIAL. The Man-o'-war-bird is pronounced by all authorities to be the most completely aerial of all sea birds. It is practically nothing but wings and tail—a span of seven to eight feet and a body the "size of a domestic cock." Their wings are so long and their legs so short that these birds rise from nests with difficulty. Many die by becoming entangled in nearby bushes.

69

SPECTACULAR. "The Boobies fished from the air, plunging headlong and with great force from an average height of fifty feet into the water almost directly. Like a great flying spear-head they strike the water and disappear in the jet of foam which spouts upward as they hit the surface. It is a more thrilling, reckless performance than even the plunge of the Fish Hawk. But the most amazing phenomenon in all this amazing scene was the action of flocks of Boobies of five hundred to a thousand birds, which, in more or less compact formation, were hurrying to join one of the Booby squalls, which darkened the air over the fishing grounds. If, unexpectedly, they chanced to fly over a school of fish, instantly and as one individual, every Booby in the flock plunged downward and in a twinkling the air, which had been filled with rapidly flying birds, was left without a feather! This spectacle, the most surprising evolution I have ever seen in bird life, was witnessed repeatedly during the day." This note was written by Dr. Frank M. Chapman.

71

ACROBATIC. The Short-eared Owl leads intruders from the vicinity of the nest with astonishing feats of flying, clapping his long wings together over his back, turning somersaults and dropping like a stone to the ground.

PHOTOGRAPHIC SUPERLATIVE. To obtain a photograph of an Owl flying is difficult enough—to secure one such as this of two Snowy Owls in flight is certainly a remarkable achievement. It was taken by Alfred M. Bailey of the Chicago Academy of Sciences. The bird has a wing span of 5½ feet. The wings are broad as well as long and the flight is characterized by slow flapping with occasional sailing. This Owl can capture birds on the wing in the manner of certain Hawks. It is heavily feathered to withstand Arctic cold, making a bulky body, whose streamlining should make an interesting study for the airplane designer who has to contend with bulk.

73

INSECTIVOROUS. Dr. Joseph Grinnell says that the present rarity of the White-tailed Kite is due to its preference for marshes, where its habit of flying slowly back and forth at a moderate height above the ground, makes it an easy target. It is a skilled acrobat in the air. It will often raise its wings above its back, so that they almost touch, and drop straight to the ground without checking speed. Hovering generally precedes these dives for prey.

CAMBERED. The part of a bird's wing that is near the body is the most concave as may be seen in this Louisiana Heron. This concavity or camber gives added lift. With the larger, slow fliers it is generally great; in fast ones such as the Swift, the wings are quite flat. The faster a plane moves through the air in the direction of flight, the greater is its power of support, and therefore the less need for camber—which accounts for much of the disparity in wing forms.

75

IN PASSING. Young Tree Swallows, like others of the Swallow Family, are fed in the conventional manner while they are in the nest, but once having left it, they are fed from the wing. The parent will fly by and drop the food into the young one's mouth in passing. When the young are able to fly this transfer takes place in the air. Certain Hawks, such as Montagu's Harrier, have been known to transfer food while in full flight, but in this instance the pass is made high above ground from one parent to another, the bird with the food dropping it a distance of five or six feet, the one below receiving the food in its talons by swinging the body backward in a half somersault.

76

REFUELING FROM THE AIR. A female Ruby-throated Humming-bird (for the male seems to take no part in feeding the young) regurgitating partially digested food into the gullet of a young one. This photograph gives an excellent idea of the direction of the wing stroke while hovering.

I have had the good fortune to watch the "pendulum" mating flight of these birds, in which the female sits on a limb and watches the male repeatedly sweep through the arc of a circle, which in this case had a diameter of about thirty feet. During the time that I was watching, the evolution was performed perhaps a dozen times before the birds disappeared.

77

AERIAL BOMB. Brown Pelicans fish in the manner of Gannets, flying back and forth at a height of twenty or thirty feet until they see a fish swimming near the surface. They then dive with half-closed wings, striking the water with great force—a resounding splash which can be heard for some distance. Pelicans, like Gannets, have air-sacs under the skin on their breasts which must

serve to cushion the shock of these dives, but which must also make them buoyant, requiring considerable momentum to carry them below the surface. They sometimes remain under water for several seconds, often reappearing tail first. Fishermen have been known to entertain themselves by tying a dead fish to a board in order to watch these birds dive for the fish and break their necks.

COOPERATIVE HUNT. Unlike the Brown Pelican, the White Pelican does not dive for its food. Instead, it forms long lines parallel to the shore and some distance out, then each bird, beating the water with its wings, drives the fish in shore, catching them near the surface or in the shallows. These Pelicans measure up to 70 inches in length and have a wing spread of 8 to almost 10 feet. Although much flapping is required to lift their heavy bodies from the water, when once launched their flight is buoyant. They will often soar to great heights, and remain there for long periods before descending.

80

STERN PARENT. For weeks after hatching—even after the young Bald Eagles are able to fly, their parents still provide them with food. But, according to W. P. Pycraft, the moment the parents believe that the young have learned to care for themselves they turn upon them and drive them from the vicinity of the nest. This seemingly unnatural conduct tends to prevent overcrowding in hunting territory and to avoid inbreeding.

The photograph above was taken by Dr. Francis H. Herrick from a steel tower eighty feet high, built especially to observe the nesting birds.

INDIVIDUALIST. The Guanaye, the Cormorant found in Peru, differs in its hunting habits from all other Cormorants, in that it searches for its food entirely from the air, first locating the fish and then descending to the water. The other members of the family dive from the surface in some likely spot, then locate and pursue their prey under water, using their large, fully webbed feet for propulsion and, at times, their half-spread wings which beat with great rapidity. The feet, when brought forward, are closed to flat blades; when pushing, are opened wide. The fact that they can catch fish in thick muddy water raises the question of whether hearing is involved in detecting them. The photograph shows the short leg and long foot of the typical Cormorant. The bird is in the act of landing—with eyes fixed on the spot.

82

UNDERWOOD AND UNDERWOOD

DEEP SEA DIVER. Loons are so much at home under water that they often dive to great depths while hunting fish. One authority has stated that a Yellow-tailed Loon was taken on a hook laid at a depth of 90 feet. They have the power of reducing specific gravity almost instantaneously and of swimming with only their heads and necks exposed. They have been known to remain under water for eight minutes. The photograph shows a Loon in the act of using wings as well as feet in an effort to obtain sufficient momentum to rise from the water. On land when making for the water in a hurry they revert to type, and wings are used as forepaws. These activities suggest the Steamer Duck, some individuals of which have lost the power of flight and use their wings as paddles to supplement their webbed feet in scuttling over the water.

ALEXANDER WETMORE. COURTESY U. S. BUREAU OF BIOLOGICAL SURVEY

HOMERS. Polynesian natives often catch Man-o'-war-birds while young, tame them and teach them to carry messages from island to island, in some cases as far distant as 80 miles. These birds are catching fish thrown in the air.

84

Migration

EVER since man became capable of reasoning he has speculated about the movement of birds—where do they come from; where are they going; what impels them to take these long annual journeys; how can they gauge the time of their arrival at different points with such precision; how can they find their way at night, in fog, across seas; how can young birds untaught and in many cases unaccompanied by older birds make their first trip and arrive at the winter home of their particular species?

For every question there have been many solutions proposed. Although we are far from being able to answer any of them completely, it is at least comforting to know that we can eliminate some of the less probable ones.

For example: One of the early theories to account for the change in bird population from season to season, was that of transmutation. According to this theory birds changed their identity for the winter, turning into other animals or other species. Aristotle believed that the European Robin (quite a different bird from our own) changed in winter into the Redstart.

Hibernation was for centuries a favored theory, based, undoubt-

85

edly, on the fact that many birds were discovered in a half-alive condition in the mud of marshes. That these birds may have fallen exhausted by fighting storms during a migratory flight does not seem to have bothered the commentators. The theory persisted and more than half a century ago, Elliott Coues recorded over 175 books and articles written about the hibernation of Swallows alone.

In 1703, "A Person of Learning and Piety" wrote a quaint treatise announcing that migratory birds flew to the moon. He calculated that it took them just sixty days to make the journey and that by directing their course at the outset straight for the moon and holding to this course the moon would meet them again at the end of the allotted time. He confidently stated that they were able to sleep whenever they wished. He did, however, hit upon one point which has been supported by modern observation. He believed that the birds were nourished by the fat on their bodies. This has been found to be true of Plovers and other similar species that travel over the sea. For several weeks before the flight these birds begin to store up fat. At the start they are covered with a thick layer of this fuel; at the end of the journey it has been burned up.

When once it was established that birds cover great distances in migratory flights, the naturalists were puzzled as to how to account for the staying powers of the smaller birds. In 1740 Gmelin wrote that it was an ancient legend among the Tartars that each Crane carried a Corncrake on its back. Like many another picturesque idea this theory has suffered at the hands of more complete information.

Today, although our conclusions are by no means final, yet, due to the increasing mass of information on the movements of individuals by banding and the work done by trained scientists on the physiological side, we seem to be approaching more reasonable grounds for our beliefs.

Perhaps the most puzzling aspect of the problem is the departure

LEGEND. According to an ancient Tartar legend Cranes assisted smaller birds such as Corncrakes in migrating by carrying them on their backs. This photograph shows the Sandhill Crane (minus the Corncrake, however, which manages to migrate independently).

in the fall of the countless hordes of young birds, which, without experience, without guidance from elders, find their way unerringly to winter quarters in the south. They are escaping from a winter of which they have had no experience to a predictable territory which they have never seen and of which they can have no possible knowledge.

Here, then, is part of the problem; another part being the equally complex initiation and completion of the return in the spring to the breeding grounds in the north.

The conditions which make an autumn movement south desirable are clearer than those governing the spring migration. Increasing cold and stormy weather, during which a bird requires more food, the shorter hours of daylight in which to forage for it, overcrowding of the breeding areas with young and old and consequent scarcity of food,—all these would seem to be adequate reasons for

87

SOUTH. Impelled by a force beyond their control these Grackles and Starlings are driving to warmer climates. An instinct so deeply rooted must have been developed many hundreds of centuries ago.

the southern trip. For the return to the north we are left with the somewhat evasive theory that it is the repetition of a search for a suitable place for breeding and for the rearing of young, yet we cannot define conclusively what suitable means. For enemies abound in the north as well as further south and feeding territory is not demonstrably better than that which they leave. Many naturalists hold that in past ages the ancestral home of birds was in the north and that the spring flight is a return to breed in this home. Even though this does not seem completely satisfactory, it is only by some such underlying theory that we can justify their leaving the tropics in the spring where food is still exceedingly abundant.

An instinct as deeply rooted as that of migration must have had its origin countless centuries ago. Looking back to the glacial period in North America, for example, we may find a clue. During the first stage of the Ice Age, the sheets of glacial ice extended as far south as New Jersey, Pennsylvania and Illinois. Gradually it receded and was followed by vegetation. As Dr. Alexander Wetmore [1] points out, certain species of birds more successful in adapting themselves to life probably produced in greater abundance than their native territory could sustain. Some were crowded into this newly opened territory. In summer, conditions were such that they were able to breed there. As winter approached and food became scarce their wanderings took them into more favorable territory to the south. This flux and reflux became a habit and regular routes were established. In those regions where the recession of the glaciers did not obtain, growths of forests, the development of fertile plains or marshes or the raising of areas out of the water may have given the same opportunity for this extension of territory and a breeding ground.

Rowan states that among the passerine species of today, the northern representatives of a majority of genera either lay more eggs to a clutch than the southern, or they rear two or more broods in place of one. He interprets this as indicating that conditions in the north are more favorable for breeding. On the other hand, nature's method for maintaining an equilibrium among animals seems to be to provide a large number of eggs or offspring where the rate of mortality is high during incubation or later. From this it might be inferred that conditions in the north were less favorable. The test is whether the northern species are actually increasing in numbers over the southern.

Among the many problems to be encountered, is the question of why so many small birds, such as Chickadees, Nuthatches, Kinglets

[1] The Migration of Birds: Alexander Wetmore.

and Creepers, perfectly able to fly further south to more equable weather conditions, remain obstinately in the north despite the dangers and discomforts of cold winter conditions. One theory is as follows: These birds are closely related to similar species found in the Old World. When the glaciers finally receded and left even Greenland and Iceland with evidences of sub-tropical climate, these species could have moved over this northern route into North America. Many families such as Wood Warblers, Vireos and Hummingbirds have no close relatives in Europe, Asia or Africa—only in Central and South America. If we explain the fall migration of birds as a return to their winter ancestral homes, it would be natural for our winter residents, being cut off from their northern route by changed climate due to receding glaciers, to remain north, while those birds which originated in the south would go south. Even with Tree Sparrows, Snow Buntings and Winter Wrens, whose families are found all over the world, the species which remain north in winter are most closely allied to European species.[2]

Considerable progress has been made in the last few years in determining the nature of the conditions which set in motion the semi-annual act of migration. There is apparently an external stimulus received from the environment, and a closely related internal stimulus which is physiological.

In discussing external stimuli, Rowan rejects the theory that failure of the food supply is the primary cause, by reference to the species which leave as early as July before the food supply has reached its peak. He rejects temperature because it is so varied in character and intensity each year, while migration movements are so regular. Barometric pressures cannot be the prime motivation, although they may be incidental. If they were, migrations would be occurring at all times of year.

[2] See The Book of Bird Life: Arthur A. Allen.

STURDY. Certain species of Humming-birds migrate all the way from Alaska to Brazil. These are Allen Hummers taken by William L. Dawson—the only photograph I have seen in which the wings of these birds have been completely "stopped" by the camera.

The seasonal fluctuation in day-length is the factor around which he has centered a most interesting series of experiments.[3] By the use of artificial light in an outdoor aviary of Juncos, he simulated the spring increase in day-length, beginning in November. This he continued until the first part of January. It had been known for some time that the migratory instinct was closely associated with

[3] The Riddle of Migration: William Rowan.

the growth and shrinking of the sex organs. In certain species the organs may weigh 1,500 times as much during the breeding season as they do in midwinter. In this instance, the birds had reached their maximum spring breeding condition by the time the experiment was concluded in January. Furthermore, it is important to note that the temperatures to which they were subjected during the seven days of most rapid growth at the end of the allotted time were 21, 31, 44, 37, 36, 20 and 4 degrees below zero Fahrenheit. This certainly disproves the accepted theory that the growth of the gonads is dependent on rising temperatures.

The next step was to discover the connection between longer (artificial) day-length and the anatomical changes in the birds. It was assumed that this was duration of the period during which the bird could exercise. Two cages were constructed, one of which was fitted with a travelling bar which swept perch and floor, making it impossible for a Junco to remain quiet more than 20 seconds at a time. The cages were placed in a shuttered room so dimly lighted at night that the birds in the cage without the bar could sleep comfortably. The cage with the bar was then operated every evening for a period of time which would correspond to increasing day-length in spring, just as had been done in the case of the artificially lighted experiment. The result on the birds was identical with the previous experiment, thus proving that it was the length of time each day spent in activity rather than the amount of light or kind of exercise obtained.

If we accept this theory we must assume that fall migrants that cross the equator and thus meet the longer days of the southern summer, have established an annual rhythm which ignores these increasing day-lengths. It is quite possible that the length of time spent in the northern hemisphere would account for this rhythm.

Having discovered a way to control the development of the reproductive organs, Rowan then attempted to find out something about the behavior of birds liberated with gonads at different stages of development. These experiments showed that those with gonads increasing or decreasing generally left the territory, while those whose organs were either at a maximum or minimum tended to remain.

Subsequent experiments made on Crows seemed to indicate that the southward passage at least, was independent of the influence of the gonads, since castrated individuals proceeded south just as normal Crows did. In spite of the fact that all Crows subjected to various experiments were liberated at a non-migratory season, almost without exception they followed the regularly established migration route, exhibiting a remarkable "sense of direction."

When we come to the question of the routes travelled by migrating birds, we are brought face to face with the problem of whether acquired characteristics can be inherited. Although this has never been proved, it is equally true that it has never been disproved. How else can we account for the initial southern trip made by the young of so many species, unaccompanied by their parents—in some cases, such as the Golden Plover, taking a route separated by as much as 2,000 miles? Why is it that Cliff Swallows migrating from South America to northern points in the United States ignore one of the most travelled air routes across the Caribbean Sea and the Gulf of Mexico? They go westward through Panama, then northwest through Central America and Mexico, 2,000 miles more than is necessary. According to Dr. Frank M. Chapman, we can only believe that they are following the route made by their ancestors.

Certain species choose one route to the south and return north by a widely separated route. Perhaps one explanation for this might be that the feeding territory offers different possibilities at different times of the year.

The arrival at the ultimate destination we can only attribute to a deep-seated sense of direction combined with a topographical memory which we know by many experiments is remarkably developed in birds.

Many attempts have been made to isolate the seat of this "sense of direction." It cannot be truthfully said that to date any have been successful.

None of the known senses seem to offer great possibilities. The very character of the nasal organ, when compared with that of animals whose sense of smell is keen, appears to be decadent. Instead of being fleshy and moist and near the end of the bill—a position the nostrils held in Archaeopteryx—they are mere openings near the base of a horny bill. In the adult Pelican and Gannet, they are entirely closed. The much discussed sense of smell in Vultures seems to have been another misconception. I understand that recent experiments on caged Vultures taught to wear the falconer's hood and thus unable to see their food, have indicated that their sense of smell, far from being keen is actually deficient.

For a sense of touch a bird must depend mainly on direct contact through feathers, since horn and scale deny them any great sensitivity in this respect.

Experiments have shown that the sense of taste is present but not highly developed.

The sense of hearing is acute, but strangely enough, in spite of their ability to sing, most birds do not seem to be as much concerned with the character as with the fact or intensity of sound. It is interesting to note that in Swifts and Swallows, whose flight is not only fast but twisting and swerving, the part of the ear devoted to balance is especially developed.

The eye has reached a higher state of development than that of a man, yet even from the greatest height at which birds have been recorded, the earth would only be visible in a radius of about two hundred miles under the most perfect atmospheric conditions. Keen sight would thus be serviceable in finally locating their destination

CAN HE SMELL? None of the known senses seem to explain a bird's "sense of direction." The nasal organ, for example, compared with that of other animals whose sense of smell is known to be well developed, appears to be degenerate. It was thought for a long time that Vultures were able to detect carrion in this way. Recent experiments with hooded birds seem to indicate that this sense is not at all keen. The picture shows the characteristic Turkey Vulture silhouette—a tail much longer than that of the Black Vulture. There is a peculiar dense look to the fore part of the wing and a translucent appearance to the after part. Notice how little the head and neck protrude.

95

and in guiding in instances where topographical memory was involved. But it could not account for flights on dark nights, through fog or on maiden voyages south. It would also be of little service in the case of Penguins which cannot rise above the surface and whose field of vision is thus limited. Yet they return annually to their breeding grounds without apparent difficulty. On the other hand, sight is undoubtedly more useful to oceanic birds having the power of flight than is generally believed. They cover thousands of miles in their wandering and can probably orient themselves to some extent by the appearance of the water—its different colors, rips, and marine life.

At the time that Dr. John B. Watson was connected with Johns Hopkins University he conducted a number of tests on Noddy and Sooty Terns which were nesting on Bird Key in the Dry Tortugas. He caught and marked with aniline dyes three Noddy and two Sooty Terns. These were sent to Key West, a distance of about seventy-five miles, and from there in the hold of a north bound steamer until they were about twelve miles off Cape Hatteras. This is distant from Bird Key about eight hundred and fifty miles in a straight line across open ocean and land. It is about a thousand and eighty miles by water. Homing Pigeons have been trained up to this distance but generally the procedure is to work them up to it by degrees, and even then it would be considered a long journey. The trip from Bird Key to Cape Hatteras took three days by boat. On the morning of the fifth day after they were released both Sooty Terns were back on their nests. One of the Noddy Terns was seen in the vicinity several days later.

Dr. Watson then sent several Terns across the Gulf of Mexico to Galveston, a distance of eight hundred and fifty-five miles. One of the birds made the return trip in six days, one in seven days and a third in twelve days. The distance between the two points is a clear stretch of water without island, reef or shoal. In spite of these tests

HIBERNATOR? Over 175 books and articles have been written about the hibernation of Swallows alone. Nevertheless, this Tree Swallow, in common with other species, solves its seasonal problem by migration rather than hibernation, according to today's evidence. In spite of all the accumulated research on this subject, we are far from having complete information on the summer and winter homes of every species. For instance, that of the Chimney Swift has never been definitely located. Identification of such birds flying above tropical forests is very difficult and they are generally out of gun shot. How powerful this instinct of migration is, may be judged by comparing it with the parental instinct. There are well authenticated instances of Barn Swallows leaving their last brood of the season to die of starvation, when once they had felt the irresistible urge to fly south.

97

FAITHFUL. A Noddy Tern taken in the Dry Tortugas. Three Noddy and two Sooty Terns were marked and shipped from here to Cape Hatteras, 850 miles distant in a straight line. On the fifth day after being released, both Sooty Terns were on their nests and one of the three Noddy Terns was seen in the vicinity several days later.

and in spite of careful anatomical investigation, no conclusion was reached as to the basis for the "sixth sense."

One of the most interesting possibilities for investigation is the relation of the earth's magnetic field to the birds' sense of direction. Just as day-length is a constant among all the variables surrounding the impulse to migrate, so the magnetic field offers a constant directional guide.

Lindbergh, in his flight to Paris, carried an induction compass, a simple device based on moving a coil of wire through the earth's magnetic field, thus generating a certain amount of current. If the plane altered its course, the coil would generate more or less current, a change which would be recorded on a dial. Ornithologists have for years discussed the possibility that birds are equipped with a sensitive mechanism similar to this which enables them to detect the earth's magnetic lines of force.

In bio-physics today, it is believed that every muscular movement and even the reception of images within the eye is no more nor less than the transmission of an electrical impulse in our nervous system. That being the case it would not seem out of the realm of possibility that certain types of animals might fit into this electro-magnetic hypothesis. It is, perhaps, significant that, upon being released, Homing Pigeons rise in great circles before starting off on their course. This suggests the possibility that they may be getting the "feel" of these directional magnetic lines.

Comprehensive experiments are lacking to support the theory. Nevertheless, several tests have been made recently which may have a bearing on it. Harlan T. Stetson in an article on this subject [4] quotes the following instance of the effect of broadcasting from radio stations upon Homing Pigeons.

"Last October 7 Mr. Paget, in company with five others, conducted an experiment in Youngstown in conjunction with radio station WKBN located on top of the Y.M.C.A. Building. Sixteen birds were released from the roof of the building early in the morning when the station was off the air—not only birds from the vicinity of Youngstown, but also some from out-of-town lofts. The sixteen birds circled but a few minutes and then were all off in an eastward direction.

"One Cleveland bird got home in two hours, flying 60 miles airline. One Pittsburgh bird got home in two hours and fifty-two minutes flying 65 miles air-line. One bird from Warren, Ohio, apparently strayed and did not reach home until the following morning, although Warren is but sixteen miles from Youngstown.

[4] "The Great Pigeon Mystery" in "This Week," March 31, 1935.

99

USEFUL. Homing Pigeons have been known to carry messages over 800 miles. They are trained up to these great distances by degrees. Many experiments have been made in an effort to determine the source of this ability. In France, birds were anaesthetized previous to their trip from the loft and were given two days to recover from the effects. When released they returned at once over a distance of 70 miles. Pigeons were used extensively during the war both over land and from sea planes. In several cases important rescues were made which were entirely due to their remarkable performances.

"Station WKBN then went on the air and sixteen other birds were released, within 100 feet of the antenna. Unlike the performance in the previous try, these birds flew around in circles for nearly half an hour, apparently finding it difficult to decide on the direction for flight. Ultimately they scattered in all directions."

Further experiments have been made at Nantes in France according to an item in the New York Times dated March 30, 1935. To quote from this article:

"Groups of pigeons were freed close to the big navy radio station, which was continuously broadcasting on a 9,000-meter wave. The pigeons showed signs of bewilderment, which increased with the strength of the broadcasting.

"Some veteran homing birds took as long as three minutes to find their direction, whereas under normal conditions, they start off within twenty seconds.

"Finally 169 pigeons were released at once when the broadcasting waves were most powerful. A majority of the birds alighted or returned after repeated failures to find their direction."

This accords with observations made on pigeons during electrical storms when they show evidences of being confused.

*   *   *   *   *

Almost as remarkable as these unsolved aspects of migration, is the patent and proveable matter of the great distances travelled. It is difficult for us to understand how so frail a body as that of a Blackpoll Warbler can transport itself back and forth from South America to Alaska—a distance of some 7,000 miles.

The Wheatear travels from Africa to Greenland—the only land bird which migrates regularly between North America and Africa.

The long distance record is held by the Arctic Tern, whose nest was discovered only 450 miles from the North Pole and whose wintering range is in seas skirting the Antarctic Continent—a distance of at least 11,000 miles. When we consider that 22,000 miles a year is involved simply in moving the base of operations, the total number flown, in foraging and migrating, becomes nothing short of remarkable.

At the other end of the scale is the Long-tailed Chickadee of the Rocky Mountains, which makes its annual trip to winter quarters by dropping down 8,000 feet to the foothills a few miles away. This is known as altitudinal migration and is a familiar phenomenon in the Himalayas, the Andes and the Rockies.

The record for what is apparently the longest ocean flight of a shore bird goes to the Golden Plover, one form of which travels from Labrador to South America and in its Pacific form flies from Alaska to Hawaii—distances of 2,500 to 3,000 miles. The Atlantic group goes all the way from Arctic America to the Argentine pampas. Honors in the Pacific group are shared with the Turnstone which also makes a direct flight from Alaska to Hawaii.

The distances covered by migrating birds, in a day, varies considerably. Professor W. W. Cooke, who made extensive studies in migration, estimates the average speed of travel for small birds passing up the Mississippi Valley at 23 miles a day. Dr. Alexander Wetmore states that the Gray-cheeked Thrush, on its 4,000 mile journey from southern United States to extreme northwestern Alaska, travels at the average rate of 130 miles a day.

Many species apparently speed up this daily rate the farther north they go. For example, the Blackpoll Warbler averages 75 miles a day through the United States and 200 miles a day through northwestern Canada.

In view of recent discoveries about the most satisfactory cruising height for planes, it is interesting to review some of the records of the heights at which different species have been seen. For those who relish figures, here is food for thought:

102

Alexander Sprunt, Jr., tells me that in the fall of the year in which the Cooper River Bridge was built at Charleston, South Carolina, 275 birds were found dead on the bridge one morning. They had dashed themselves against it in the dark. Many others must have fallen into the water during the night. It was estimated that 3,000 birds were killed in a period of 3 weeks. Since that time no such extensive catastrophe has occurred there. This raises the question of whether migrating birds learn the location of these obstacles as they remember the topographical features of the countryside.

In this connection it is interesting to note that the Washington Monument, which is over 500 feet high, used to cause the death of hundreds of small birds flying at night in bad weather. Since 1910, under similar conditions, the casualties have not been as numerous, until the fall of 1932 when hundreds died in this way. Phoebe Knappen, who has made a study of these conditions believes that the recent casualties have been due to the lighting on the shaft of the column.

The great contribution which bird banding has made to the study of migration can hardly be estimated.

The marking of birds has been practiced from time immemorial. The earliest definite date for a banded bird, according to F. C. Lincoln of the Bureau of Biological Survey, is that of a Heron captured in Germany in 1710 with metal rings on his leg, one of which had been placed there in Turkey several years prior to the date of capture.

In America, we know that birds were banded as long ago as 1803, for Audubon relates having marked a brood of Phoebes and actually having obtained records of two returns.

At the end of June 1932, there were almost 2,000 people on this Continent alone, cooperating in this work. The total number of birds banded had risen to 1,123,528. Out of this number 63,564 had been retrapped during or following the succeeding migration period

TRANSOCEANIC RECORD. The Golden Plover holds the record for the most spectacular ocean flight of any shore bird. Two forms migrate from Labrador to South America and Alaska to Hawaii, respectively—distances of 2,500 to 3,000 miles. The possibility that they may alight on the water to rest or that the Eastern form may find land en route scarcely detracts from the remarkable performance. Before leaving, they fatten themselves to provide fuel for the journey—at the end there is generally little left.

or had been killed and recovered—a truly remarkable record of more than one bird out of twenty.

By plotting the increasing mass of return records on the map a more accurate picture of the movement of each species is obtained.

Some of the long distance returns are of interest in showing the worldwide scope of the work. As might be expected, the Arctic Tern holds the record. One, banded as a nestling on the coast of Labrador on July 22, 1927, was found dead near La Rochelle, on the west coast

ACCIDENTAL. Buffle-heads, normally residents of North America, have been recorded in the British Isles. Although some species of birds are inclined to wander more than others, the chief reason for birds being seen out of their natural territory is that many are carried off their course by storms. Each hurricane that sweeps up the coast carries with it numbers of birds which belong further south. This photograph, taken by Dr. Allen, is unusual in that it has caught two birds at exactly the same point in their wing beat.

of France, on October 1, 1927. Another Tern, banded as a Common Tern on July 3, 1913 in Maine, but now believed to have been an Arctic, was found dead in South Nigeria, West Africa, in August 1917. The longest flight on record for any banded bird, is that of an Arctic Tern banded as a nestling July 23, 1928 at Turnevik Bay, Labrador and found on the beach at Margate 15 miles southwest of Port Shepstone, Natal, on the east coast of South Africa, on November 14, 1928. The shortest possible distance between points is 8,000 miles and the probable course would be around 9,000 miles. Considering that the bird was less than four months old, this is a remarkable performance.

A Laughing Gull has been reported 2,000 miles from the banding point, Caspian Terns 2,500 miles, and Black-crowned Night Herons 2,300 miles.

Bird banding is also throwing some light on the age of birds. Among smaller species the records show from 4 to 9 years. One Pintail adult banded in September 1913 was killed in October 1926, making a minimum age of at least 13 years.

It has been discovered that birds adhere closely to their ancestral flyways. This has been demonstrated not only by the regular returns but by an interesting experiment in which several shipments of banded birds, chiefly Pintails, were made from Louisiana to widely separated points and released in spring. During the season of 1933–34 there were retrapped Pintails that had been liberated at Washington, D. C.; Cambridge, Md.; Cape Cod, Mass.; Berkeley, Cal.; Voltage, Oregon; and Moiese, Mont. These birds had deserted the Atlantic and Pacific flyways where others of their kind were quite common and had returned to the Mississippi flyway and their original winter quarters.

* * * * *

There are still many unsolved problems which neither food supply nor sex impulses, homing instincts nor meteorological conditions can account for separately or together. We cannot with certainty put our finger on the basic reasons for the movement, nor do we know why a bird will elect to remain in one place instead of pressing on to another. The mystery of the initial trip of the young to winter quarters remains.

These problems can only be solved by combining the knowledge gained from such sources as bird banding with further research in bio-physics and bio-chemistry.

A KING EXHAUSTED. This Duck Hawk alighted on the *S. S. Birming-ham* on one of her trips between New York and Savannah. As this type of Hawk is one of the strongest flyers among all birds, the storm must have been severe. The Duck Hawk is the Peregrine Falcon of the days of chivalry.

DUCK HUNTER'S DREAM. Thousands rising, thousands still to rise from a preserve on Lake Washington. Of all species that have been banded, the Mallard has yielded the largest percentage of returns due to the number of reports from sportsmen. The Black Duck is next in number. In the last few years the census of Wild Ducks shows a deplorable decrease.

PINTAIL. Pintails banded in Louisiana and sent to such distant places as Maryland, Massachusetts, California and Oregon were later retrapped in Louisiana. They had left the Atlantic and Pacific flyways where others of their kind were common and had returned to their original winter quarters. Dr. E. R. Kalmbach of the United States Bureau of Biological Survey is here shown releasing a Pintail at the Survey's station at Klamath Falls, Oregon.

EARLIEST BANDING RECORD. For years men have marked birds in order to obtain some record of their wanderings. The earliest definite date for a banded bird is that of a Heron captured in Germany in 1710, having metal rings on its leg, one of which had been placed there in Turkey several years before. This Heron (Ardea Cinerea) is similar to the Ward's Heron shown in the photograph, which in turn corresponds to the Great Blue Heron. The bird shown is leaving its perch on the top of a mangrove. Every inch of sail area is being used. The legs have not yet been drawn up and stretched to the rear.

114

TRANSATLANTIC. A Black-headed Gull banded at Rossitten, Germany, was taken subsequently at Bridgetown, Barbados. Another from the same point was taken at Vera Cruz, Mexico. The Laughing Gulls in the photograph resemble in appearance the common Black-headed Gulls found in Europe.

H. EMERSON TUTTLE

115

HIGHEST. A scientist photographing the sun at Dehra Dun, India, obtained a picture of Geese at an estimated height of 29,000 feet—almost 5½ miles high. The photograph, taken by Alfred M. Bailey, shows Snow Geese migrating.

BIRD'S EYE VIEW. Sandhill Cranes migrating, taken from an airplane by Gene A. Howe and John L. Mc Carty. The Cranes are evidently in great confusion. Aviators' records of the height of flight of these birds during migration vary all the way from 1,625 to 8,000 feet. The direction and strength of the wind is undoubtedly an important factor governing the height at which they fly.

WORLD-WIDE. The Turnstone nests as far North as 70° and goes south throughout the world as far as South Africa, Australia, New Zealand and Chile. Turnstones and Sanderlings have a greater migration range than any other bird, for they appear at one time or another on almost every seacoast throughout the entire world. They reach islands more than 800 miles from any continent. Captain Donald B. McMillan records that he saw a large flock of Turnstones alight on the water in Kennedy Channel. This suggests that they may rest on the long over-seas flights, and raises the question of whether the Golden Plover's flight from Alaska to Hawaii and Labrador to South America is actually non-stop.

The Turnstone shown here was photographed at $\frac{1}{680}$ of a second, yet one wing was not stopped. The bird rose from the sand into the wind, then turned to the right. It has apparently banked a little too steeply and is regaining equilibrium by a deeper, quicker stroke of its right wing. The quick changes in direction made by birds of this type are effected by this unequal use of the wings. How a flock of them can execute simultaneously the flashing maneuvers so natural to Plover and Sandpiper is a nice matter for speculation. Undoubtedly a quickness of eye superior to our own makes them aware of the slightest change in direction of the bird adjacent to them. Whether or not they communicate by sound is not only debatable, but also difficult to determine.

118

119

OCEAN MIGRANT. Wilson's Petrel, "Mother Carey's Chicken," is the smallest web-footed bird known. It measures only 7 to 7½ inches in length. Like the Shearwaters it reverses the usual migratory movement. It breeds in extreme southern latitudes and migrates across the Equator through the oceans of the entire world with the exception of North Pacific. How they find their way over the ocean and back and forth from these different points is still a mystery. The photograph shows them patting the surface of the water with both feet—their characteristic habit in calm water or when feeding. It is this walking on the water which is supposed to have given them St. Peter's name. Their legs are so ill adapted for use on land that they cannot perch or even stand upright without the aid of beating wings. It is said that Petrels are often used by the inhabitants of certain islands in place of candles, their bodies first being threaded with a coarse wick, the oily layers of fat serving as tallow.

LIMITED VISION. The Penguin presents another problem to the student of migration. In traveling back and forth from their breeding grounds the range of vision of these birds is strictly limited, as they cannot rise above the surface of the water to get their bearings as other birds might be expected to do. We are forced to the theory that they depend on their "sense of direction."

Gulls exhibit this same ability in flying in dense fog. They are aided by no sense of touch, they are handicapped by a sense of smell which is inferior to most animals. Perhaps at times they may use their sense of hearing if there is a surf running to guide them to land, but this cannot help them far off shore. Their sight is limited by the density of the fog.

The Galapagos Penguins in the photograph are entertaining themselves in the Aquarium at Bermuda. Nature abhors the showy Swan dive and approves the beginner's more modest method of slinking in with a minimum of display.

FARTHEST NORTH. The most northerly record for any bird is that of the Ivory Gull found in the Polar Sea at 85° North—less than 350 miles from the Pole. There have been many exaggerated tales of birds following ships for great distances—the difficulty being that replacements may be mistaken for the original birds. However, it seems possible that Kittiwakes have actually followed ships across the ocean since birds marked with rings as nestlings on the coast of England have been taken in Newfoundland and off the coast of Labrador. This photograph, taken in Alaska, shows the Glaucous-winged Gull.

I have watched five Kittiwakes riding out a hurricane in mid-Atlantic. The birds tried to keep within the lee of the ship which actually offered little protection. They kept as close as possible to the water, although there was a cross sea which piled the water up in huge pyramids. Their speed over the water was terrific, and they never gave the impression that they were having an easy time. They were "masters of the air," as bird writers like to put it, by a very small margin.

They were there under their own power, however, which was not the case with the two Crows which joined the Empress of Britain 750 miles out of Southampton and rode, literally, in the Crow's nest, leaving only when the ship had made a complete crossing and had entered the Strait of Belle Isle.

123

EFFORTLESS. With little apparent exertion the Glaucous-winged Gull glides or soars, wings advanced in rising, flexed when gliding to gain speed.

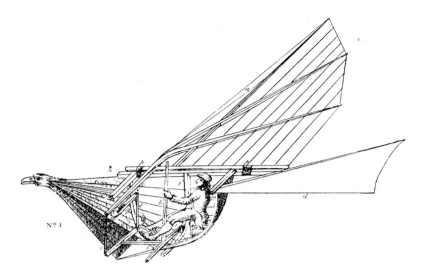

EARLY EFFORT at flapping flight. From a book written in 1810 by Thomas Walker, the portrait painter, on "The Art of Flying."

Aerodynamics

THE East Indian gentleman who declared that he was not interested in horse racing because it had been demonstrated long ago that one horse runs faster than another, was expressing an indifference comparable only to that of the ornithologist who neglects the subject of flight on the grounds that it is common knowledge that birds fly. The vast literature on birds seems to divide itself into the text books of description, many for the purpose of identification, and the popular literature which has done so much to stimulate the interest of the amateur. Flight itself, which, after all, is a bird's most characteristic feature has, for the most part, been left severely alone. There have been many good reasons for this, the chief among which is

125

G. C. A.

UP AND DOWN. A Mockingbird in fast horizontal flight, in
which the wing is moved nearly straight up and down. This is the
beginning of the down-stroke with feathers spread to form the largest
air-resistant surface. Notice the large overlap of the secondaries.

that so little has been understood about it. What the ornithologist has failed to study in a spirit of pure science, the engineer in aeronautics, stimulated by practical needs and commercial necessity has come to investigate. His findings, however, are expressed in a convenient language all his own, useful for those who have traveled the laborious way with him, but unintelligible to those who have not. Somewhere between the normal interest of a man in a bird and the specialized interest of an engineer in aerodynamics lies an absorbing field of observation.

There are, in general, three types of flight—flapping, gliding and soaring. Flapping flight, naturally, is effected by the up and down movement of the wings resulting in support and propulsion. Gliding involves sailing on set wings with loss of height; soaring adds the element of a gain of height.

The first and commonest form, flapping, is not quite so simple as it appears to be. If anyone not acquainted with the intricacies of flight were asked how a bird flies, the answer might very naturally be that the bird simply beats its wings up and down. If pressed further for a reason to explain specifically how the bird is able to move forward, he might reply that the bird probably rows itself through the air, reaching up and forward and pushing the air downward and backward.

Actually, this is not the case. The simile of rowing does not hold. It is rather the principle of an airplane propeller, but in this instance, the two blades move in semicircles and adjust themselves to one angle on the down-stroke, and the opposite angle on the upstroke. The beat is rarely straight up and down—probably it is only so in swift horizontal flight. In flapping flight of normal speed the movement is more upward-and-backward, downward-and-forward.

This is the part that is particularly puzzling to the layman—that a bird should move forward or upward by bringing his wings downward and forward apparently beating against the direction of flight. This action is clearly shown, however, in the photograph of the Mourning Dove and in some of the Pigeon and Gull pictures. The extreme in this angle through which the wings move is

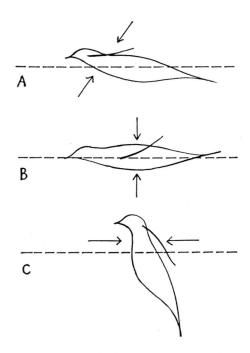

FIGURE 1. A. Position of bird and angle of wing-beat in slow horizontal flight. B. In fast horizontal flight. C. In hovering.

found in hovering or in steep rising, where they appear to travel almost backward and forward rather than up and down.

The backward push, then, is due to the angle at which the wing is held during the down-stroke rather than the direction of the stroke itself. During this stroke the forward margin of the wing is lower than the rear margin. It falls naturally into this position because the forward part contains the activating bones and muscles and the force of the air pushes up the trailing edge which is unsupported. The force of the wing-beat acts at right angles to the surface of the wing and resolves itself into a downward and a back-

128

RISING. Upward-and-backward, downward-and-forward is the rule for rising flight. This California Gull is beginning the up-stroke. Inner secondaries and tertials are still affording support, as is the tail.

ward component—one giving lift to the bird and the other forward movement. This forward tilt of the wing on the downbeat can be clearly seen on birds whose shoulders rotate freely, such as Crows. This effect is emphasized when flying fast or against a strong wind.

It is, naturally, the up-stroke which is the big problem in the economy of flapping flight. This is partially solved by the construction of the wing itself. The convex upper surface allows the air to slip off with a minimum of resistance, the flight feathers separate and allow air to pass through them, and the size of the resistant

129

CLIMBING. 1. Pigeon slapping wings together overhead. The down-stroke has just begun, judging from the first primary. The rear view of an almost identical position in the top bird of number 3. 2. Completion of down-stroke, wings well forward. Compare this position with that of the Mourning Dove, page 179. 3. The lower bird is just coming into the same position as that in number 2. Notice the twist in the wing, secondaries at one angle, primaries at another.

area of the wing is reduced by a partial folding of the wing itself.

Another factor is the timing and position of the wing as it is raised. Slow motion picture films of Swans in flight show that for these birds, at least, the down-beat takes half again as long as the up-beat. The wrist is raised first, the primary feathers following parallel to the direction of raising for some distance, after which they are raised with a quick flip. This is shown in the accompanying photographs of Mallards.

Still another advantageous feature in the execution of the up-

130

UP-STROKES. The Pigeon photographs on these two pages were all taken at ⅛₂₅ of a second. Those on the opposite page showing downstrokes have almost "stopped" the motion. The one above shows how fast the movement is at this point in the up-stroke. Wrists are moved straight up over the back and the outer half of the wing is then snapped upward and backward. The primaries of the bird at the left have opened to let the air through. The right wing is moving backward.

stroke is that the wing is being carried backward automatically by the pressure of the air due to the bird's motion.

I obtained one photograph of a Mallard, making a short flight in still air to a landing on the water, in which the primaries on the up-stroke are shown not only separated but curved at such an angle as to indicate that they are actually driving the air backward and downward. If this takes place to any appreciable degree then a bird may be said to *scull* his way through the air—a metaphor which is further strengthened by the fact that flapping flight in-

131

HELICOPTER. The Humming-bird is the only land bird that can fly backward, and one of the few birds that can rise straight up into the air. The body in hovering is dropped below the angle of normal flight, and the down-stroke becomes an almost horizontal forward-stroke. The bird shown in the photograph is a Rufous Humming-bird.

volves the use of half-revolutions, just as in actual sculling.

E. H. Hankin whose book "Animal Flight" contains many careful observations on birds, says that there appears to be little room for doubt that in horizontal flapping flight a propelling effect results from both the up and down strokes of the wing. Marey, also, found that in the flight of insects, propelling work was done both on the up-stroke and on the down-stroke.

The shape of the wing in illustration Number 2 on the cover would bear out this theory. It illustrates not only the sharp rotation of the wing from the shoulder and the bending at the wrist, but

132

also the relatively high speed of the up-beat at this point. Each picture represents an identical lapse of time, and consequently shows the extent of the development of the stroke from stage to stage.

FIGURE 2. The path taken by the tip of a Crow's wing in rising. The diagram should be read from right to left. After a photograph by Marey. Notice the shape of the bottom loop.

Among the many experiments devised by Marey years ago in his efforts to analyze flapping flight, was one which has always seemed to me particularly ingenious. He attached a piece of white paper to the wing-tip of a Crow which he placed in front of a black screen. He then opened the shutter of his camera and released the Crow. The result was a white line which drew a perfect diagram of the movement of the bird's wing tip. The first strokes took the form of a figure 8—the lower loop being very small. As the bird proceeded, the lower loop disappeared.

Although birds utilize the same principles in flying, their application of them varies widely. Some idea of the great divergence in the speed of wing beats for example, may be gained from the following table.[1]

Humming-bird	Up to 200 strokes per second.
Sparrow	13 " " "
Swift	10 " " "
Duck	9 " " "
Pigeon	8 " " "

[1] Compiled from figures taken from Hilzheimer, Hankin, Marey and Bodine.

Marsh Harrier	5¾	strokes per second.
Screech Owl	5	" " "
Green Parrot	5	" " "
Carrion Crow	3–4	" " "
Blue Jay	3⅓	" " "
Buzzard (Hawk)	3	" " "
Paddy Bird	2½	" " "
Black Vulture	2½	" " "
Cheel	2¼–2½	" " "
White Scavenger Vulture	2¼	" " "
Adjutant	2–2¼	" " "
Heron (cinerea)	2	" " "
Stork	2	" " "
Pelican	1⅙	" " "

These figures are to be considered rather for their relative than their absolute values, for the speed of wing beat is altered by wind conditions and by such simple human reasons as flying in a leisurely way after a heavy meal, or being in a particular hurry to get to feeding grounds. I have watched a Black-crowned Night Heron under the latter circumstances fly with a beat half again as fast as the normal beat, under the same wind conditions as his mates who had preceded him to feeding grounds by several minutes.

It is interesting to notice that in the above table the general rule is that the larger the bird, the slower the wing beat. The exceptions, if not inaccurate, appear to be due to a difference in "loading," that is, the relation of sail area,—wings, tail and under body —to weight. The Duck at 9 strokes a second and the little Screech Owl at 5 a second would be an example of this apparent discrepancy. The great difference in the loading of different species is indicated by the fact that a Golden-eye Duck, heavy in body and with a small sail-area, is represented by the figure 2.85, while a Barn Owl is 6.735.

Any discussion of the speed at which birds fly leads to debatable figures. The methods used in determining speed vary in the degree

134

of inaccuracy. Automobiles running on parallel courses, airplanes, measured courses and stop watches, allowances for wind and no allowances for wind—with results which give a bird considerable latitude.

Among the more reliable investigators is Col. Meinertzhagen, a British aviator, who has made a number of records by airplane and with surveying instruments designed to estimate the speed of airplanes at anti-aircraft stations.

He states that the Swift, the fastest of birds, can increase the speed of 70 miles an hour at which it often feeds to a velocity of over 100 miles per hour. A. L. Thomson says that Swifts of a common species feeding 6,000 feet above Mosul, were recorded as circling with ease about an airplane which was making 68 miles per hour. Another much-quoted report is that of an aviator who went into a nose dive with a Lammergeier, a large Vulture, at 110 miles an hour.

E. C. Stuart-Baker reported that while in India he timed two species of Swifts with stop-watches over a two mile course and found that they covered the distance at 171.4 to 200 miles per hour.

The record estimate for a bird's speed, I believe, is that made by Gätke, who spent fifty years at Heligoland studying birds and their migration. He argued that great speeds were possible in high altitudes due to more rarefied air, a theory we know to be borne out in the contemporary practice of aeronautics. Certain air liners, for example, have found that an economical height for cruising under certain conditions is around 12,000 feet. Gätke believed that such birds as the Plover, Curlew and Godwit attained speeds up to 240 miles per hour at altitudes of 40,000 feet. Naturalists are inclined to doubt his figures.

In casual observations made from an automobile running parallel to the line of flight, I have recorded Starlings at 35; Bronzed Grackles at 35; a Boat-tailed Grackle (male) at 28; a Red-winged Blackbird at 28; a Robin at 36.

MALLARDS, male and female, caught at $\frac{1}{680}$ of a second about 15 yards before landing on a pond. The wing-tips move fast at the top of the stroke.

The down-stroke well under weigh. A faint indication of the stiff outer primaries being bent by the pressure of air. The tail is short compared to the length of the body.

The full down-stroke, difficult to see with the naked eye—blurred even for the high speed camera. To the eye, a Duck appears to make only a narrow arc when flapping.

G. C. A.

The start of the up-stroke, wrists already on the way up, but primaries still bent from rounding off the down-stroke. The whole wing is contracting.

A close-up of the middle of the up-stroke, wrists well up, with primaries separated and curved in such a way as to suggest that they are actually *pushing air backward*.

The bird's right wing is about to make the fast upward flip just executed by the left wing, which can be seen in two positions at once—an indication of the speed of the upward flip.

The table below has been compiled from various sources. It represents specific records, not the range of speed for each bird.[2]

Arkansas Kingbird	10–17 miles per hour
Scissor-tailed Flycatcher	10–17 " " "
Song Sparrow	17 " " "
European Blackbird	Over 22 " " "
Missel Thrush	23 " " "
European Cuckoo	23 " " "
Willow Warbler	23.5 " " "
Pied Wagtail	25 " " "
Northern Flicker	25 " " "
Baltimore Oriole	26 " " "
Boat-tailed Grackle	28 " " "
Red-winged Blackbird	28 " " "
Bronzed Grackle	27–35 " " "
Herons, Hawks, Horned Larks, Ravens and Shrikes	22–28 " " "
Crane	30 " " "
Crow family	30–45 " " "
Finches	30–33 " " "
Robin (American)	22–36 " " "
Rook	32 " " "
Great Blue Heron	35 " " "
Pigeons	26.1–36 " " "
Crossbill	36–37.5 " " "
Smaller Perching Birds	20–37 " " "
Swallow	34–37.75 " " "
Pheasant	34–38 " " "
Jackdaw	38–39.6 " " "
Sand Grouse	43–47 " " "
Falcons	40–48 " " "
Starling	35–49 " " "
Albatross	49 " " "
Waders	34–51 " " "
Geese	42–55 " " "
Ducks	44–59 " " "
Swift (European and Asiatic)	70–200 " " "

[2] Idrac, Thomas, A. A. Allen, G. M. Allen, Gladstone, F. B. White, Meinertzhagen, Thienemann, E. C. Stuart-Baker and those of my own referred to above.

It is possible to trace several underlying principles in the body and wing design of the fastest birds such as Swifts and Duck Hawks. The bodies are beautifully stream-lined—the entire body of the Swift being torpedo-shaped and the Duck Hawk having a noticeably perfect blending of the outstretched wing into the body. The wings are long and narrow—in the language of the airplane designer they have a high "aspect ratio" that is, the relation of length of wing to "chord" or breadth. In one specimen of a Swift which I measured, the length of the wing along the forward margin was just over 4 times the width taken through the middle of the secondaries and 6 times that taken through the widest part of the primaries, the wing being in flying position.

There are two other factors which seem to be associated with speed—a pointed wing and little camber. In the Swift the under surface of the wing is quite flat compared, for example, with that of a slow-soaring bird such as a Red-shouldered Hawk.

There are many designs of wings, each one efficient for the duties placed upon it by the different species. Swifts, Swallows, Falcons, and Humming-birds have narrow and pointed wings—the Swallow's being broader at the base than the Swift's. The Nighthawk's, while long and pointed has a noticeable bend at the wrist, a position characteristic of fast gliding. A Meadowlark, rising from and landing in meadowgrasses would be handicapped with this type of wing. Instead, its wings are short and comparatively rounded. Sparrows and the smaller birds that dart through underbrush must, of necessity, have short, rounded wings. For the same reason Pheasants, Quail and Grouse have developed this type of wing. The slower, soaring hawks, such as the Red-shouldered and Red-tailed have very broad wings. Gulls on the other hand with an unobstructed range, have pointed wings, efficient for remaining in the air with a minimum of effort, yet designed for fast gliding. The Tern's, even more Swallow-like in shape, enables it to hover and

139

200 STROKES A SECOND. Certain authorities estimate that the wings of a Humming-bird execute from 600 to 1000 strokes a minute. Others, however, by comparing the vibrations of a violin note with that of a Humming-bird's wings, have estimated that they move at the rate of 200 beats a second. The Black-chinned Humming-bird above, is in the act of whipping its wings backward in the up-stroke.

make flashing dives. And the Penguin has not been overlooked in the adaptation of wing design to function. It now possesses a completely adequate flipper.

One type of flapping flight deserves particular mention—that of the Swift. It is the only bird, so far as I know, which beats its wings alternately instead of in unison. For one species, and that the fastest, to reverse the normal practice in this way is certainly worth more study than has been given it to date. There has been some discussion as to whether this actually occurs or not, most ornithologists pre-

1⅙ STROKES A SECOND is sufficient to propel the enormous Brown Pelican through the air. Even the gigantic Pterodactyls of by-gone ages, with a wing spread of 18 feet, are estimated to have weighed less than these birds. Notice how the feet are carried.

ferring to say that they "appear to beat their wings alternately." A moving picture has been taken which shows that the wings move in unison. This is not surprising for it is quite possible that such might have been the case at the time the picture was taken. Apparently they do fly in this way for short distances, mainly when on a straight course, but the moment a turn is involved, alternate beating again takes place. This statement may seem somewhat dogmatic considering the fact that there are differing opinions, but continued observation of Chimney Swifts flying at low altitudes and in many cases with greatly retarded wing-beat has convinced me that most of their flight is made with alternate beats.

C. J. Maynard has described the method by which Swifts enter a chimney. Balancing themselves for a moment over the opening they raise their wings above their heads and drop down, avoiding too rapid a descent by "oscillating the body from side to side." This seems an entirely natural action for birds whose bodies must oscillate in a similar way, (but one less easy to observe), while flying with alternate beats.

For a bird of slow wing-beat to stroke alternately would surely be awkward. The high frequency natural to the Swift makes it possible, and provides the best method for making the quick changes of course necessary in catching insects at 60 or 70 miles an hour.

This matter of changing course raises the question of the function of the tail. Here, in the Swift, is an example of a bird to whom instantaneous changes are essential, yet its tail is small and apparently useful chiefly because its stiff spines provide an excellent prop to be used on verticle surfaces.

Hankin, from his observation of tail-less Cheels (a species of Kite) came to the conclusion that they were mainly handicapped in landing and in steering in a horizontal plane. He believes that the effect of the tail as a rudder in the horizontal plane has been exaggerated, pointing out that a bird when gliding downward often

142

has his tail furled and raised, and when making a landing his body is rotated at right angles to the line of flight, yet the tail is depressed. These movements are so complex and so swift, however, that it seems probable that the tail shares both balancing and steering functions—for example, steering at the inception of the movement and balancing as the action progresses.

It is difficult to discover what effect the shape of the tip of the tail has on skill in flying. A Magpie with a spade-shaped tail, a Flycatcher with a moderately rounded one, a Sharp-shinned Hawk with a tail that is squared off, and a Barn Swallow with one that is deeply forked—all are adept at maneuvering.

A short tail, however, is a decided handicap in making quick turns. Birds with tails of this character, such as Ducks, usually have a very direct flight. Birds with extra long ornamental tails are equally handicapped. The male Wydah bird, if exposed to heavy dew, actually loses the power of flight because of the extra weight on its exaggerated tail.

Perfect muscular control enables a bird to raise, lower or spread its tail, lower one side or the other, make it concave or convex. Notice for example, the picture of the Fulmar. Headley in "The Flight of Birds" shows a photograph of a Pigeon in which the tail fully spread to 180°, appears to be rotated at right angles to the line of the shoulders.

The tail is capable of altering the direction of flight upward or downward by merely opening or closing. By spreading the feathers, the center of the plane of suspension formed by the wings, body and tail is moved back. The center of gravity is thus relatively advanced. To illustrate, a bird flying in a horizontal plane with tail furled, spreads the feathers. His direction is altered downward since he has more support toward the rear.

In steering to the right or left the bird must move its center of gravity to one side or the other of the center of suspension. It can

143

EXTREMES IN LOADING. Above, a Golden-eye Duck; body heavy in relation to its sail-area of wings, tail and under-surface of body; stiff pinions that whistle as they beat 9 to the second. Below, a Barn Owl, silent in flight, only half as fast in wing-beat; a sail-area of 6.735 to the Duck's 2.85. Notice the steering action of the Owl's wings—left wing forward and up, right wing still down and somewhat back, to offer less support on that side.

200 MILES AN HOUR, according to E. C. Stuart-Baker who timed Swifts with a stopwatch over a two mile course. Most authorities agree that no bird flies faster. The Swift is distinguished not only for its speed but also because it is probably the only bird that beats its wings alternately. Stuart-Baker's record was of two Asiatic species, not of the Chimney Swift shown here.

lower one side of its tail, turn its head to one side or partially flex one wing, or it can do all of these at once. The use of the tail in turning seems to be to a large extent in the nature of an equilibrator, since the tail may sometimes be seen depressed on the opposite side from the direction of turn—evidently a corrective movement.

Rapid rising or falling to avoid an obstacle is due not only to the action of the tail but also, to movements of the shoulder joints forward or backward. When the wings are advanced, the bird rises; when they are retarded, he dives.

In long-necked birds, such as the Swan and the Heron, the center of gravity may be shifted by an adjustment of the neck. A Heron in getting under weigh or in attempting to fly fast, will extend his neck fully from the retracted position used in ordinary flight.

In hovering a bird assumes a position with tail depressed and expanded. If there is wind the bird naturally faces it. I have watched a Sparrow Hawk hovering in a moderate breeze on the windward side of a stone wall perhaps 25 feet from the ground. Due to the ris-

145

ing current deflected by the wall, he was able to remain stationary on outstretched wings for intervals of a second or two. His wing-beats between those brief periods of sailing was between 4 and 5 beats to the second.

Certain naturalists have stated that hovering is impossible if there is no wind to furnish a succession of unbroken columns of air under the wings, but, certainly, Humming-birds hover in places completely sheltered.

Those birds which hover most frequently do so in the course of hunting. All of these birds, such as Hawks, Owls, Gulls, Terns, Kingfishers and others of their kind are notably strong flyers.

The Kingfisher, when hovering in comparatively still air beats his wings almost forward and backward. The backward stroke, which is really the up-stroke, has a supporting effect in that the front margin becomes the leading edge so that the upper surface of the wing faces downward and backward.

In rising, as has already been noted, a bird expends many times the energy used in sustained, straight flight. A Pigeon, whose flight is exceptionally strong, if made to rise and fly for a short distance five or six times in succession, will finally remain on the ground panting, with beak open. How necessary it is for birds to face the wind in rising may be seen by watching the Sparrows rising from the road in front of an automobile. If they are toward the lee side of the car they risk flying in front of it before turning away to leeward.

Certain short-legged, long-winged birds, in the absence of wind, cannot rise at all from the ground without a protracted run. Audubon, a century ago, quotes his friend Townsend concerning the California Condor, "When about to rise they always hop or run for several yards, in order to give an impetus to their heavy body, in this resembling the Condor of South America, whose well known habit furnishes the natives with an easy mode of capturing him, by

146

FURLED; SPREAD. This photograph of Man-o'-war-birds shows
how active the tail is in this extraordinary flyer. The wind conditions are presumably identical, the direction of flight similar,
but the tails are all the way from tightly furled to fully spread.

means of a narrow pen, in which a dead carcass has been depos-
ited." Today, a century later, they are captured in the same way.

The thing which all birds must have to rise is this initial velocity
relative to the air. If the air does not move sufficiently in relation to
them, when still, they must move in relation to the air. The funda-
mental physical law underlying the flight of a bird is this: The gain

147

BALANCE. Nature has achieved perfect balance in a wide variety of forms—the Black-necked Stilt, whose statuesquely long legs must be offset; the Spoonbill, large of wing, long of neck, short of tail; and the Hooded Merganser whose small braking area is supplemented by its webbed feet. These peculiarities are developments closely related to the securing of food. Yet, in the course of evolution, the important requirement of balance in flight has not been sacrificed.

148

in resistance of the air to the wing stroke or the extended wing *increases with the square of the velocity* of the bird's flight. When once this fact is understood it becomes apparent how a bird, once launched, is able to make such speed through the air. As Darwin puts it: "The force to keep up the momentum of a body moving in a horizontal plane in the air (in which there is so little friction) cannot be great; and this force is all that is wanted."

Sir George Cayley, over a century and a quarter ago, in a study "On Aerial Navigation" worked out a specific example. He found that a Rook, whose weight and wing-area [3] were roughly a pound to a square foot would be able to glide horizontally whenever it attained a speed of a little over 25.4 miles per hour. This gliding could not, of course, continue in still air in a horizontal plane.

The angle of descent of such birds as Ducks or Pheasants whose loading is high, would undoubtedly be greater than that of any of the soaring birds.

Sail-planes, unembarrassed by provisions for cumbersome motors, have been perfected to such an extent that a gliding angle of 1:20 was reached some years ago. It is interesting to see how efficient a structure of this kind may be made when its only requirements beside a good gliding angle are that it be strong enough to stand up under the strains of starting, soaring and landing. The bird's requirements of flapping, parking of the wings against the body, and carrying a self-contained engine and the apparatus for refueling, are dispensed with.

This matter of the gliding angle is important as it has a direct bearing on the most interesting aspect of a bird's flight—soaring. By soaring is meant gliding on outstretched wings with a gain of height. Throughout the years there has been a prolonged discussion of the means by which a bird is able to soar. Professor Roy of Cambridge whose article on "Flight" in Newton's "Dictionary of Birds" has be-

[3] Cayley did not allow for the area of the body measured in the plane of flight.

149

NOT A MACHINE. Only a living organism could exhibit the freedom of motion shown in the wings of these Bank Swallows. A wide variety and a great number of muscles make this freedom possible throughout the body of a bird. It has been estimated that there are, under the skin of a Goose, twelve thousand muscles whose only function is to control the action of the feathers. It is little wonder that man has been unable to refine a machine to such a degree.

150

FLEXIBLE CONTROL. The Fulmar above is holding its tail in the convex position, probably in order to gain lateral stability, a conjecture supported by the fact that the feet are extended to the sides. The angle of the feet opposes that of the tail. Birds have remarkable control of their tails. They can spread them, furl them, raise and lower them, rotate them on both a horizontal and perpendicular axis and make them either concave or convex in shape.

151

come a classic, states that explanations of soaring flight so far are "insufficient." Lord Kelvin, when asked if he could explain these phenomena, replied, "That which puzzled Solomon puzzles me also."

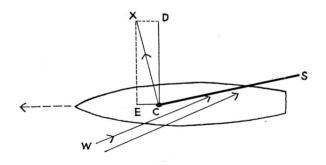

FIGURE 3. Sailboat moving to windward. W Direction of wind. CS Angle of sail. CX Force of wind which acts at right angle to sail. CD That Part of force CX which tends to make leeway. CE That part of force CX which gives forward drive.

Dr. Manfred Curry, who has made extensive studies of wind conditions and in particular of the aerodynamics of sails, believes that the secret of soaring flight is based on three things—the increase in wind velocity which comes with an increase in height, the so-called upward direction of the wind, and the excellent aerodynamic design of the bird's wing. This "upward direction of the wind" is a theory, originally proposed by Lilienthal, I believe, to the effect that the wind does not blow in an exactly horizontal direction, but at an angle of 3° or 4° upward. Dr. Curry explains this as being due to the suction effect exerted by the greater velocity of the higher layers of air on the lower ones. Lilienthal, however, explained the theory by saying that air in a high-pressure region passing to a region of low-pressure encountered an area of motionless air, which, tending to resist, became dense and escaped upward at an angle with the horizontal. This explanation would certainly limit the upward tendency to restricted areas in which the above conditions existed.

152

TAKE-OFF. Compare the wing position and structure of this American Egret with that of the Pigeon in the picture opposite. The head is being drawn back toward the body after having been extended as shown in the frontispiece. Long legs must balance long neck.

a bird in only a slightly rising current to set its wings horizontally and move forward with a speed dependent upon wind and angle.

Due to the fact that the surface friction over the water is less than over land, the speed of the wind is far greater over the former than over the latter. Fifty feet above the water the wind is traveling about three times as fast as it does just above the surface. For example, an

155

Albatross finds that he is losing height and speed while gliding at the surface. He uses his remaining velocity to gain height and in a distance only four or five times his wing-spread, he encounters air traveling at three times the force of that he has just left.

A mission of the French scientist, Idrac, to the South Seas to study this problem found that this type of soaring flight was only possible for very swift birds, the average speed of the Albatross being 72 feet per second or 49 miles an hour. A minimum wind speed of 17 feet a second was necessary close to the water.

Dr. Curry's third point—that the form of a bird's wing is a major factor, has been studied intensively in an effort to perfect sailplanes. It is claimed that there are planes which can, theoretically, outsoar any bird. In practice this is naturally difficult to demonstrate, since it is impossible to know whether a soaring bird is making every effort to gain height. It is interesting to note, however, that on one occasion Lewin Barringer soared beside a Turkey Vulture for ten minutes and finally outclimbed him.

The efficiency of the bird's wing in soaring is dependent on several factors—its aspect ratio, that is, the relation of length to breadth; its shape in plan; its camber, or curvature fore-and-aft; its "slotting," the spacing of the outer primaries when extended, and other minor points.

The aspect ratio of the average bird is about 3:1. In the Albatross it may run over 5:1. We find the aspect ratio of airplanes today up to 7:1 where structural requirements hold the figure down, while in the most efficient sail-planes they have risen to 16 and 18:1. I understand from Edward P. Warner of the Advisory Council on Aeronautics that except for consideration of the undue increase in weight and the dangers of structural failure, it would be advantageous to increase the aspect ratio without limit.

Soaring birds, however, such as Eagles, Vultures, Pelicans, Storks, Falcons, Kites, Buzzards (Hawks), Ravens, Gulls, Frigate-birds and Albatrosses have other considerations than simply those of soaring. Their aspect ratio is more conservative. It is true that there is a surprising variation between species, but their type of flight is equally different.

According to the law of Avanzini, a plate falling vertically through the air meets the maximum of resistance at the center, the resistance decreasing toward the margin. If the plate falls obliquely, the maximum of resistance moves to the forward end of the plate. This end, therefore, has a tendency to tip up. This is true of a flat surface, and it is even more true of an arched surface, such as a bird's wing.

By loading the wing of a freshly killed bird with a weight of sand equal to half the weight of the bird Dr. Curry approximated the arching of the wing while gliding. The average measurement of the wing arching of good flyers showed a depth of curvature of $1:15$, that is $1/15$ of the breadth of the wing at the point of deepest arching. The slower birds showed $1:10$ to $1:12$.

This curvature has a very subtile form, differing at different sections. It serves not only to afford lift to the bird while gliding or soaring, but because of the angle of the anterior margin of the under side of the wing, it exerts a definite backward thrust in flapping flight.

Lilienthal, in an effort to find out how this camber affected air currents, constructed a machine of revolving curved planes. To the under side of each plane he attached small streamers. The streamers for a considerable distance from the front edge of the plane blew— not to the rear—but forward. This eddy only became marked when a speed of 5 meters per second was reached. This corresponds to the average minimum speed of a bird's flight. Dr. Curry notes that there is a "feather pocket" on the under side of the wing which opens up even to an angle of $45°$ in a reasonably strong current of air. The opening of this to meet the eddy under the wing is aided by the wind

157

AIRMASTER. The highly mobile tail of the Condor is an important factor in its flight. The tail of the Albatross, on the other hand, is negligible, and its wings are its sole method of steering. The Condor is loose-jointed like the Crow; the Albatross, rigid. The Condor can soar in air in which the Albatross would be forced to flap—a paradox, in that the Albatross weighs only half as much as the Condor yet has a comparable wing spread. This indicates the importance of the design of the wing. The photograph was taken by Dr. Robert Cushman Murphy off the coast of Peru. A fine study in wing positions.

HANDICAPPED. Many long-winged, short-legged birds find it difficult or impossible to rise from flat ground without a considerable run. An Albatross, for example, can be caught on hook and line from the deck of a ship by using salt pork for bait. The hook lodges in the bill. When released on deck, the bird cannot escape as it has not room enough for the lengthy run necessary to rise above the bulwarks. The birds shown below are Laysan Albatrosses.

pressure on a tendon on the fore part of the wing which acts directly on the movement of these feathers.

It remained for aeronautic engineers to discover how important a sustaining factor was the suction created by a bird's wing. We think of a bird as gliding through the air by virtue of the support afforded by the under side of the wings. Actually, as in a sail boat, the negative pressure or suction is approximately twice as great as the positive pressure.

The difference in pressure on the two sides of a plane was clearly demonstrated by the aviator who tore the top covering of his wing to bits during a dive, while the under surface was not injured in the least. The force of suction had done this, while the pressure from below had not been sufficient to do any damage.

Eiffel was the first to establish the surprising fact that a square plate develops the greatest pressure—not when the wind strikes the plate at right angles, but at an angle of 38°. At this angle the positive pressure is only *one-half* that at 90°, but the suction is *three times* as great, which combined makes a larger total force.

It is believed that the serrated rear edge of a bird's wing formed by the projecting individual feathers, is of assistance in forming small, evenly distributed eddies to offset the large eddies caused by the relative vacuum over the bird's wing, thus avoiding the drag caused by a margin that might be too abrupt.

There is one feature in the wing construction of certain soaring birds which cannot be overlooked—namely, the "slotted" wing-tip. It appears mainly among such birds as Eagles, Vultures, Pelicans, Cranes, etc., whose wings are relatively broad with rounded or squared wing-tips. It does not appear in long, narrow, sharply pointed wings. The "slots" are formed by the gaps between the primaries of the outstretched wings. It is not only the normal spreading of the feathers which makes the slots, but the peculiar shape of the primaries concerned. These feathers are full width for perhaps half

160

SPOT LANDING. The precarious position of the Stork's nest and
the lack of concern of the young one over what appears to be an im-
pending crash, suggests that an accurate and gentle landing is the rule.

161

their length and are then stepped down to almost half width for the outer half of the feather. A feather of this type is said to be "emarginated." An ingenious friction surface on the web prevents their opening beyond a certain point.

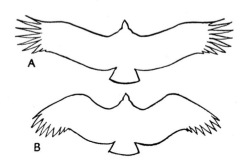

FIGURE 5. A. Black Vulture with wings outstretched and advanced in soaring flight. B. Wings flexed in fast gliding flight.

Lieut. Commander R. R. Graham, R.N. has written an interesting report [4] of a study of slotted wing-tips. He believes that as a bird glides or soars at low air speeds and is forced to increase the angle of incidence, as this angle reaches the stalling limit, the slots act as automatic anti-stalling devices in somewhat the same way as the Handley-Page slotted airplane wing. The emarginated feathers, as can be seen in several of the accompanying photographs in this book, bend upward and forward, deflecting the air over the top of the wing in such a way as to keep it flowing steadily instead of "burbling" in eddies. This means that the main part of the wing can actually be several degrees beyond the stalling angle and yet function properly. Sir G. T. Walker estimated that the angle of incidence for the wing of a Vulture gliding slowly was as high as 28°.

Mr. Handley Page, without knowing that slots of this type existed in birds' wings, designed a model plane with seven slots, arranged

[4] Safety Devices in Wings of Birds: Lieut. Commander R. R. Graham, R.N.

much as those of the Eagle, and found that it increased the maximum lift by 250% at an angle of 42°.

During the last fifteen years great progress has been made by sailplanes, in gliding and soaring, and from a study of their behavior some light has been thrown on the soaring of birds. The restrictions placed upon powered aircraft in Germany shortly after the war turned both scientists and sportsmen to gliding. The greatest developments have consequently come from that country and such astonishing duration records as 13 hours and 35 minutes and distance records up to 300 miles have been made.

We have learned the meaning of "static soaring"—soaring in upward currents of air. These rising currents may be deflected from the slopes of mountains; or they may be "thermal" currents rising because certain kinds of terrain are heated by the sun to a higher temperature than other parts. Every cumulus cloud is the top of such a column of rising warm air. Or they may be currents of warm air pushed upward by a "cold front" of descending cold air. Gliders have been flown under almost every kind of wind condition—even in gales up to 45 miles an hour. They have been flown into the face of storms on the rising currents caused by them.

FIGURE 6. A primary feather of a Black Vulture showing the narrowing of the web to form the notch between feathers.

Gliders have learned to use the variation in the speed of different layers of horizontal currents of air—those at the surface being retarded by friction and those at higher altitudes moving at higher speed. Gliders are learning more about "dynamic soaring"—which makes use of the variations in the velocity of a horizontal wind.

The principle of static soaring is simple. It is merely gliding down

163

in a rising current of air. The plane will rise in just the degree that the vertical component of the rising current exceeds the minimum rate of descent of the plane.

Dynamic soaring is not so simple and is more difficult to utilize. It involves flying in a gusty stratum of air in which the wind is at one moment increasing and at another decreasing. For example, a glider is flying into the wind at a given speed. The wind accelerates, and, using his inertia as a lever, much as a boat uses its keel, he is able to gain height by this acceleration. Any acceleration of the wind he feels as a puff in the face; any deceleration as a puff from behind. If he turns his plane completely about-face just as the deceleration takes place, he can utilize his speed and this decrease in wind speed, as a lifting agent. In practice, however, it is difficult to determine the moment when deceleration will set in, and a turn involves loss of speed.

It is probable that birds avail themselves of this type of energy since they are adept at maneuvering. The diameters of the circles in which they soar would then be an indication of the structure of the gusts, which appear to come with a certain rhythm.

As we come to know more and more about the structure of the air, those secrets of a bird's flight which even now remain will drop away one by one.

Man's insatiable mind, goaded on by a handicapped body, will undoubtedly invent subtleties and refinements for his present clumsy progress through the air; but in spite of all he can learn from a bird, he will never attain that mastery of the air which is the result of the development of millions of years acting on the self-contained mechanism of a living body.

*   *   *   *   *

AERODYNAMICALLY CORRECT. That a bird such as a Stork, thrown together in so slip-shod a manner, should have sufficient mastery of the air to be able to soar, is simply a proof that it is the fundamentals of design that count, and not the superficial appearance. A good illustration of "wing-slots."

166

"SLOTTED" WING. The peculiar "fingered" effect of the wing-tips of this Lesser Spotted Eagle taken by Horst Siewert, act, according to some authorities, like the slots in the wings of the Handley-Page airplane. The slots in the wing of the airplane open as the plane approaches the stalling point. They serve to divert the air stream over the top of the wing in such a way that the wing remains effective beyond the ordinary stalling point. In the same way these primary feathers, sharply narrowed down for their outer half, render the wing more effective. They not only bend upward at the tips because of lack of mutual support, and in this way aid in directing the stream over the wing, but each feather assumes a different angle in relation to the horizontal, as may be seen in the photograph. The first primary, near the forward edge of the wing appears much narrower than the others. This is due largely to the angle at which it is seen, for while the main wing is facing down and a little forward, this feather and the others following in lesser degree, are facing backward as well. This effect may be seen in the photograph of the Stork with wings raised.

167

ROCKETING. A Mallard rising, taken by Chauncey Powers, and considered by "Field and Stream" through whose courtesy it is reproduced here, as the most remarkable photograph of a flying duck received in that office. There are few things more spectacular than this almost perpendicular rise of a river duck from the water. First, consider that the bird is heavily built for the size of its wings, and that quite a portion of its body is below water. From the sitting position the bird could not flap its wings in such a way as to gain height without beating the water. This means that it must *leap* out of the water. Even with the advantage of webbed feet, the Duck's legs are short and water is scarcely an ideal footing from which to take off.

The extent of the splash made by this Mallard is proof of the power of its leap and gives some idea of the angle at which these Ducks can rise.

168

UP. It takes strong, stiff pinions to lift the body of a Mallard out of the water. It is all the more surprising, therefore, to find that in the duckling the wing remains in the downy state until the rest of the body is practically covered with feathers. Even the bones of the wing are retarded at this stage. This is just the reverse of the chick of the barnyard fowl whose body is still downy when the wings are feathered. In aquatic birds the emphasis is laid on swimming and diving as a means of escape for the young, rather than speed over the ground.

VAULTING OUT. A remarkable photograph of Black Ducks rising made by George Shiras 3d. One bird has thrown himself even beyond the 90° angle in an effort to clear the water. There is a thrill in watching a flock of these birds leap out of the water nearby with a roar of wings and a scatter of spray.

STARTLED. The Pintail is one of the most intelligent and wary of all the Duck family. As the photograph shows they rise as abruptly as the Blacks. The Coots in the picture are alert but have not moved off, while the first Pintail is yards away. Although it is a surface-feeding Duck it dives with ease and has been known when wounded to cling to objects on the bottom to avoid capture.

172

SKITTERING. The Canvas-back, in sharp distinction to the Black, the Mallard, and the Pintail, paddles along the surface before rising. The latter are surface feeders, the Canvas-back, a deep water feeder, with extra large, broadly webbed feet set well aft for diving and swimming. How fast these paddling strokes are made and how far apart, may be judged from the photograph.

173

TREADING WATER. The photographs on these two pages show Ducks at various stages in rising. The Blue-winged Teal on the opposite page, when alarmed, can rise straight up, but in the present instance is taking off like a sea Duck. It is one of the fastest flyers of the Duck family.

The Scaups in the picture below this are making the water boil in their confusion to be off. They must paddle for a considerable distance before they can rise. During the excessive cold of the winter of 1933–34, rafts of these Ducks stretching for over a mile could be seen in Long Island Sound. They came in closer than usual to shore in search of food. I counted over 1,800 in one float, 600 in another and 800 in still another.

The Ring-necked Duck above is not drumming but is actually on the point of beginning his pattering take-off over the water. This picture shows the extent to which a Duck of this type must straighten up before starting.

175

THIEF. An Osprey leaving its nest. Alfred J. Meyer, the photographer, told me that he knew a farmer who was astounded one day to see an Osprey swoop down, catch in his talons a waistcoat hanging on a nearby fence post, and disappear with it. A search was made but without success, and much to the farmer's chagrin, for, attached to the waistcoat was his gold watch and chain.

176

EUROPEAN. The Osprey is one of the most widely distributed birds of prey. The European species differs from our own mainly in its breast markings, being a slightly darker bird. Incidentally, the word "osprey," as used in the feather trade to describe the egret's nuptial plumes, is derived from the French word *esprit* and has nothing to do with the Osprey or Fish Hawk.

COMMERCIAL NOTE. At the beginning of the latter half of the 19th Century the average annual exportation of Guano from one small group of Peruvian Islands averaged twenty to thirty million dollars. Cormorants or Guanayes form a large part of the bird population of these islands. Dr. Murphy, who took the above photograph, says that when they are traveling toward distant feeding grounds, they move over the water as an almost solid river of birds. A single stream of them may take four or five hours to pass a given point.

178

FASTEST PHOTOGRAPH. Professor Harold E. Edgerton and Mr. Kenneth Germeshausen, of the Massachusetts Institute of Technology, took this photograph of a Mourning Dove at the amazing speed of $\frac{1}{75,000}$ of a second.

This speed has made it possible to study in detail the conformation of the primaries during the down-stroke—their elasticity and perfect accommodation to the strain of the stroke. The photograph demonstrates clearly that the down-stroke is just the opposite from a rowing stroke, particularly in a rising bird.

179

THIS SERIES from a moving picture of a Laughing Gull shows how much flight of this type depends on the movement of the outer half of the wing. The inner half serves as a supporting plane to a large extent while the outer half supplies the driving force. The white line indicates diagramatically the progressive path of the tip of the wing from picture to picture. The black line shows

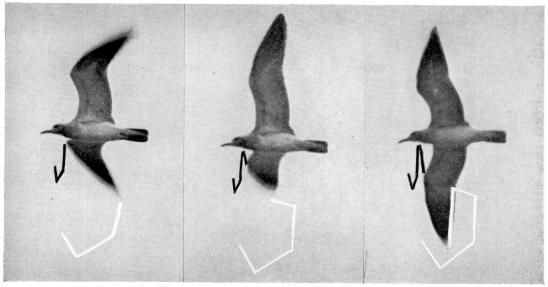

the path of the wrist or bend of the wing—in other words the tip of the inner half of the wing. Allowance must be made for the fact that the diagram is
a plan of a motion seen in perspective. Also that the bird's body is pointing
slightly upward in the first picture and is level in the last. Taking these into
account, the relative speed of the different parts of the stroke is apparent.

BIRD—THEN GHOST.

A picture of a Louisiana Heron, taken with a 12-inch telephoto lens when the bird was balancing on the top of the bush in a high wind—interesting in motion, Mr. Arthur says, because it shows the bird's ease of balancing. It was apparently unnecessary for the Heron to bend his legs to any great extent to obtain a spring, but when the leap was made from the flexible branch the legs were straightened to their utmost.

STANLEY C. ARTHUR

182

PATRIARCH. The largest bird of the order Passeres— the Raven. Over two feet long and with a wing spread of over 3 feet. Bold, sagacious—a worthy head for the shrewd, intelligent Crow family. The Raven has one peculiar trick in flying. Occasionally he will close his wings and roll over sidewise on his back in the very middle of a period of ordinary flight. I understand Ravens will also execute this maneuver if harried by Hawks.

WILLIAM L. DAWSON

MINIMUM OF EFFORT. Black Skimmers making their way straight into a gale. They are flying with little up-and-down motion to the wings. From this point of view the most noticeable action is the flexing of the wrist.

ANGEL WINGS on demon body. That the African Vulture, so hideous in appearance, should be gifted with an unequaled power of soaring is one of nature's paradoxes. Hankin, in India, made this interesting discovery: In fine weather there was a definite time, varying from day to day with the season, at which soaring began. Each species began soaring in the exact order of their loading—those with the greatest sail area for their weight beginning first.

184

185

EQUILIBRIUM. A Laughing Gull picking up food on the wing—and at the same time keeping both his wings and tail completely clear of the water.

186

BALLAST. European Osprey carrying nesting material. Audubon says
the Bald Eagle can lift from the water anything less than its own weight.

HUMBLE. Few bird photographers have bothered to photograph the flight of the English Sparrow. As a matter of fact, it is considerably easier to take the larger and more spectacular birds which do not move with such speed. These photographs were taken by Lemuel Lincoln with a Contax and a telephoto lens at one-thousandth of a second. From a standing start the Sparrow can attain remarkable speed in a relatively short distance. Part of the start depends on a leap into the air. I have watched a Tree Sparrow, startled from a window feeding box which had a rim of only half an inch, leap straight up at least four inches before flying off. This leap, of course, was aided by the wings.

188

The area of a bird's wing is considerably in excess of what is required for flight. An experiment has been made in which more than half of the secondary wing feathers of a Sparrow were cut off parallel with the long axis of the wing. The bird's flight was unimpaired. Not until more than one-third of the wing feathers were cut off, did the Sparrow show any real difficulty in flying.

Experiments of this sort have also been made on dragon-flies. It is an interesting fact, from an aerodynamic point of view, that when a dragon-fly's wings were bisected along the long axis, its flight was scarcely impaired. When the wings were bisected along the short axis the insect was not able to fly.

189

DISEMBODIED SPIRIT. There is something etherial about the White or Love Tern which seems to remove it from this world. An English writer, some years ago, expressed his belief that soaring was due to "levitation"—a miracle by which a man can remain unsupported in the air. According to this observer, the bird so alters "the magnetic polarity of the physical frame that in lieu of being attracted it is repelled by the earth." This power comes from "living an absolutely pure life and intense religious concentration." It must have caused this writer some concern to fit such a bird as a Vulture into his scheme.

LARGEST TERN. The Caspian is the largest member of the Tern family, measuring two feet in length, and with a wing spread up to four and one-half feet. Their flight is strong, their dives powerful like that of the Gannet. Captain B. F. Goss reports that upon approaching a colony of these birds, they rose, and after hovering over their nests, plunged down upon them piercing the eggs with their beaks. At least a quarter of the eggs were broken in this way. The only explanation, suggested by one of the party who had seen this happen before, was that the Terns did this to prevent the eggs from being stolen.

MAJESTY. The Gray Sea Eagle or White-tailed Eagle preys upon Puffins, Guillemots and other sea fowl as well as fish, hares, sheep, Grouse, Ptarmigan and carrion. Notice how wide open the wing slots are even with a flexed wing.

CHECKING. A European Osprey looking at the moment like an experimental tailless glider. The tail, however, is functioning, and the wings are greatly retarded as though in the backward position of a horizontal stroke.

193

VALUE OF SUCTION. A Catbird in fast horizontal flight. One reason why a bird can make such speed through the air is that the angle of the wing on the down-stroke is such that it exerts not only a positive pressure with its under side but a strong negative pressure or suction with its upper side. According to Eiffel, a square plate moved through the air develops the greatest pressure not at an angle of 90°, but at 38°. At this angle the positive pressure is only ½ that at 90°, but the suction is 3 times as great, making a greater total force.

ANCIENT. A scene which, with superficial differences, such as the race of the man and the breed of the bird, undoubtedly took place in China 4,000 years ago. Falconry was practiced throughout many of the Asiatic countries, later spreading to Europe and to England, where it was introduced about 860 A. D. It flourished there until the middle of the 19th Century. This photograph shows an immature Bald Eagle coming to the falconer's fist. The jesses of light leather may be seen attached to the legs. Notice the large braking surface.

195

ESCAPE. This series of pictures shows a Coot being chased by a motor boat. The bird, unable to outdistance the boat by flying and unwilling to leave the water and turn to one side, finally dives. This is often its method of escape when

196

STANLEY C. ARTHUR

attacked by Eagles or the more powerful Falcons. It is remarkable that the bird required no preparatory checking of speed. It has dived while traveling at full-tilt. The bird's feet have apparently touched the water first.

197

DESCENDING. A study of a Laughing Gull parachuting to the water.

198

SCIENTIFIC. Guanayes in formation, each avoiding the other's air-stream.

199

T. GILBERT PEARSON. COURTESY NATIONAL ASSOCIATION OF AUDUBON SOCIETIES

LUNGS ON TOP. The wings of a bird are inserted far up on the thorax so that the center of suspension is considerably above the center of gravity. In addition, the heavy organs such as stomach, liver, heart and the pectoral muscles are placed low, while the lighter parts—lungs and air-sacs—are above. The bird in the photograph, taken by Dr. Pearson, is a Reddish Egret.

ARCHED. The camber of a bird's wing differs in each type of bird—good flyers having a curvature of about 1 : 15, that is, ¹⁄₁₅ of the breadth of the wing at the point of deepest arching. Slower birds show 1 : 10 and 1 : 12. The Franklin Gull belongs to the former type. It closely resembles the Laughing Gull in appearance, but migrates up and down the middle and western flyways.

APOTHEOSIS. Probably the most perfect form of gliding and soaring is found in the Albatross. His evolutions are executed in air, which, on several counts, is less suited to soaring than that over the land. Land soarers can take advantage of upward currents deflected from the slopes of mountains and from warm air currents rising over certain types of ground. The Albatross, in place of these, uses the vertical pulsations over waves and the great variation in air speeds found at different heights over the water.

An Albatross will generally take off from the water in a slanting direction against the wind, make a large semicircle in the position shown in the photograph, then descend down-wind gathering momentum. Upon turning again into the wind it transforms speed into height. According to Idrac, a wind of at least 11⅗ miles an hour is necessary for these birds to soar near the surface. Due to the relative lack of friction offered by the water, the wind is about twice as fast as over land, and increases in speed at higher levels considerably faster than over land. An Albatross, losing height and velocity at the surface can mount to a height of 50 feet and find there wind moving at about 3 times that at the surface.

Part of the secret of the ability of the Albatross to soar lies in the shape and proportion of the wing, whose length is often over 5 times the average breadth. The bird in the photograph is of the Light-mantled Sooty variety.

203

"STOP-FLAPPING." A Jackdaw a split second before landing. The wings on the down-stroke are usually fully extended. This acts automatically through a set of tendons to increase the arching of the wing to its maximum.

204

RARE. Although in the last few years there appears to have been a slight increase in the numbers of the California Condor, considerably less than a hundred have been located. On these birds hangs the fate of the species.

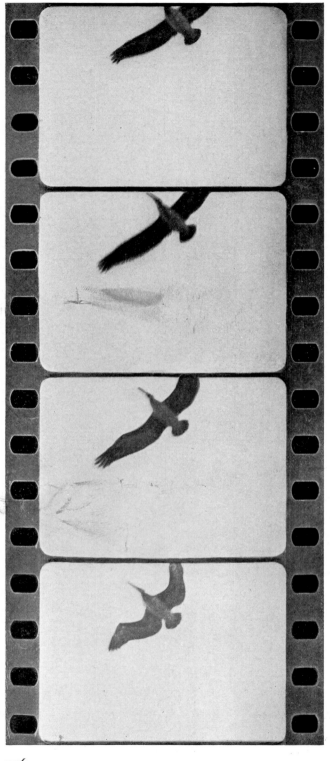

1. The down-stroke of a Brown Pelican. An early stage. (Compare length of wing with Number 2.)

2. The Power Drive. Wings slightly more forward. Greater spread at this stage indicated by blur of wings toward tip. Apparent flutter of separated primaries at end of wing.

3. Extreme downward position with beginning of bending at wrist. Primaries at widest separation.

4. The great difference between Numbers 3 and 4 indicate how quick the motion is at this point. Wrist and elbow sharply bent. Angle at shoulder very marked. Reduced wing surface to avoid unfavorable resistance to the air.

5. Increased folding at wrist. Straightening at elbow just beginning.

6. Quick straightening at the elbow and beginning of forward motion of wing-tip.

7. Down-stroke not quite as far along as in Number 1. Wrist still slightly bent. Blur of primaries as in Power Drive (Number 2).

8. Fully extended on down-stroke. Clear separation of primaries. A position evidently a fraction of a second before Number 3.

STANLEY C. ARTHUR

FAMILY FAILING. The problem of alighting has proved too much for this Farallon Cormorant—he has missed his footing. After catching a fish the Cormorant has to bring it to the surface before swallowing it. It is this habit which has led fishermen in China and India to use them for fishing. A leather collar is put around the bird's neck to prevent his swallowing the fish.

ARRESTED MOTION. This Herring Gull photographed by C. L. Welsh shows the perfect command of body and air apparently so lacking in the Cormorant. Flapping to check speed before alighting is necessary in calm air, but against a fair wind a Gull can come to a full stop simply by "braking" with outstretched wings and tail. A Gull can fly forward and *backward*.

FRANK M. CHAPMAN

INTERNATIONAL. It is apparent from the similarity of these two photographs that the method by which an Osprey lands on its nest is the same in any country. The picture opposite was taken by Dr. Frank Chapman of an American Osprey on Gardiner's Island; (the one above, taken by Horst Siewert, is the European species). If a bird finds that he has checked too soon he can reduce sail-area by raising his wings so that the secondaries become inoperative, the primaries remaining extended for lateral control.

212

LARGER AND LARGER. It is little wonder that the Fish Hawk's nest grows to such proportions with the constant replenishing of material. The care birds give their young during the nesting period is unceasing. A House Wren has been recorded as feeding its young 1,217 times during the daylight of one day. Under good hunting conditions, birds of prey sometimes bring home so much food that the surplus has to be stacked at the side of the nest.

213

STREAM-LINED WING. The wing design of this Royal Tern is such that it is equally effective aerodynamically whether in the flapping or gliding position. The inner part of the wing is so shaped that the innermost secondaries come to a point. This is a perfectly adequate stream-line device. When the wing is in the gliding position, the gap between these inner secondaries and the body is closed forming another stream-line shape.

The Royal Tern, in Eastern North America, is second in size only to the Caspian Tern. The white forehead is the typical nesting plumage, the fine black cap being a phase identified with courtship. A. C. Bent reports that he has counted one hundred nests in a space of four square yards.

214

OUTCAST. That Vultures are regarded as neither fish nor flesh is indicated by the remark of a little colored boy who followed me around while I was photographing. Upon explaining to him that I was taking pictures of the birds, he replied, "White man, dem ain't birds, dem's buzzards."

The Vultures which used to haunt the market districts of Charleston, South Carolina, and which infested the city dump, are becoming relics of the past. A new city incinerator has robbed them of their livelihood. Poison has been put on the dump to kill the rats; the Vultures have eaten the rats. I saw the skeletons of four in one spot. This Black Vulture is one of a score that still roost in the water tower overlooking the dump. He is flapping, not gliding.

215

RHYTHM. Pelicans generally fly by alternately flapping and gliding in unison; high before a favoring wind, but low when flying against the wind.

H. EMERSON TUTTLE

CALM in outward appearance, but inwardly perturbed. A Common Tern attacking an intruder at the nest. Notice the furled tail and tapered wings.

217

218

G. C. A.

F   I   N   I   S

BIBLIOGRAPHY

The American Eagle, Francis Hobart Herrick. New York, London: D. Appleton-Century Co. Inc., 1934

Animal Flight, Ernest Hanbury Hankin. London: Iliffe & Sons, Ltd., 1913

Aristocrats of the Air, C. W. R. Knight. London: Williams & Norgate, Ltd., 1925

Autobiography of a Bird Lover, Frank Michler Chapman. New York, London: D. Appleton-Century Co., Inc., 1933

The Biology of Birds, John Arthur Thomson. New York: The Macmillan Co., 1923

The Bird, C. William Beebe. New York: Henry Holt & Co., 1906

Bird Banding in America, Frederick C. Lincoln, Smithsonian Report for 1927, Pages 331–354

Birds: an Introduction to Ornithology, Arthur Landsborough Thomson. New York: Henry Holt & Co., 1927

Birds in Flight, William P. Pycraft. London: Gay & Hancock, Ltd., 1922

Bird Islands of Peru, Robert Cushman Murphy. New York: G. P. Putnam's Sons, 1925

The Birds of California, William Leon Dawson. San Diego: South Moulton Co., 1923

Birds of Massachusetts and other New England States, Henry Howe Forbush. Massachusetts Department of Agriculture, 1925, Vols. 1, 2, 3

Birds of the Ocean, William Backhouse Alexander. New York, London: G. P. Putnam's Sons, 1928

Birds of the World, Frank Hall Knowlton. New York: Henry Holt & Co., 1909

The Bird Study Book, T. Gilbert Pearson. Garden City, L. I.: Doubleday Page & Co., 1917

The Book of Bird Life, Arthur Augustus Allen. New York: D. Van Nostrand Co., Inc., 1930

Concerning the Flight of Gulls, Alexander Forbes. "The Auk" Vol. XXX, 1913, Page 359

A Decade of Bird Banding in America. A Review by Frederick C. Lincoln, Smithsonian Report for 1932, Pages 327–351

A Field Guide to the Birds, Roger Tory Peterson. Boston: Houghton Mifflin Co., 1934

The Flight of Birds, Frederick Webb Headley. London: Witherby & Co., 1912

The Hawks of North America, John B. May. New York: National Association of Audubon Societies, 1935

228

BIBLIOGRAPHY

How to Study Birds, Herbert Keightley Job. New York: Outing Publishing Co., 1910

The Human Side of Birds, Royal Dixon. New York: Frederick A. Stokes Co., 1917

Key to North American Birds, Elliott Coues. Salem, Mass.: Naturalists' Agency, 1872

The Migration of Birds, Thomas Alfred Coward. Cambridge: University Press, 1912

The Migration of Birds, Alexander Wetmore. Cambridge: Harvard University Press, 1927

My Tropical Air Castle, Frank Michler Chapman. New York: D. Appleton & Co., 1929

Notes on the Flight of Gulls, William Brewster. "The Auk" Vol. XXIX, 1912, Page 85

On the Wings of a Bird, Herbert Ravenel Sass. New York: Doubleday Doran & Co., Inc., 1929

The Origin of Birds, Gerhard Heilmann. New York: D. Appleton & Co., 1927

The Riddle of Migration, William Rowan. Baltimore: The Williams & Wilkins Co., 1931

Safety Devices in Wings of Birds, Lieut. Commander R. R. Graham, R.N. Smithsonian Report for 1932, Pages 269–305

Sidelights on Birds, H. Knight Horsfield. New York: D. Appleton & Co., 1923

Soaring Flight, Wolfgang Klemperer. Smithsonian Report for 1927, Pages 221–241

Ten Years' Gliding and Soaring in Germany, Walter Georgii. Smithsonian Report for 1930, Pages 273–283

The Travels of Birds, Frank Michler Chapman. New York: D. Appleton & Co., 1916

The Waterfowl Flyways of North America, Frederick C. Lincoln. Circular No. 342, January 1935, United States Department of Agriculture

Wild Life in the Tree Tops, C. W. R. Knight. London: Thornton Butterworth, Ltd., 1921

Wonders of the Bird World, Richard Bowdler Sharpe. New York: Frederick A. Stokes, 1898

Yacht Racing: The Aerodynamics of sails and racing tactics, Manfred Curry. New York: Charles Scribner's Sons

I N D E X